SEACOAST PLANTS OF THE C[illegible]

FOR CONSERVATION AND BEAUTIFICATION

KARL E. GRAETZ

PLANT MATERIALS SPECIALIST

U. S. DEPARTMENT OF AGRICULTURE
SOIL CONSERVATION SERVICE

Raleigh, North Carolina
Columbia, South Carolina

February 1973

This work is partially sponsored by NOAA Office of Sea Grant, Department of Commerce, under Grant No. 2-35178 and the North Carolina Department of Administration. The U. S. Government is authorized to produce and distribute reprints for governmental purposes notwithstanding any copyright notation that may appear hereon.

University of North Carolina, Sea Grant Program, School of Public Health, Chapel Hill, N. C. 27514

Sea Grant Publication UNC-SG-73-06.

CONTENTS

SECTION 4

SECTION 5

SECTION 6

INTRODUCTION

Rivers and lakes have beaches, but in this part of the world if someone says, "let's go to the beach," he invariably refers to that strand of sand where the "low country" meets the Atlantic Ocean. And in this affluent civilization, more and more people are heading that way to build their second home - a dream cottage by the sea - which in the minds of many, is framed in a setting of luxuriant vegetation. This vision of greenery can lure even the greenest thumb to disaster.

At the ocean side, the hinterland rules of plant selection, use, and culture are subject to drastic revision. Many of the local nurserymen along the coast are fully aware of these amendments. Their help with beach plantings can be invaluable. Nevertheless, many cottagers will decide to take on this job as a "do it yourself" project.

It is our hope that this publication will be of help to those uninitiated who accept these challenges - even though they may not recognize them as such. To increase its value to the average reader, technical terminology has been cut to a minimum.

Those who need advice are encouraged to call on the local district conservationist of the Soil Conservation Service who can be of great assistance. This would include pre-planning the cottage site to take best advantage of the native vegetation, and advice on plantings needed for sand stabilization and permanent protection and beautification of the area.

In gathering information on beach plants, a special effort was made to talk to many seaside gardeners (almost all ladies - some in white tennis shoes and one in her father's old forestry jacket). These conversations were enjoyable and informative. Beach nurserymen were also generous in "talking shop." The author wishes to thank them all for their thoughts, many of which have become a part of this publication.

Some of the information is based on results of test plantings of woody plants at Fort Macon and Hammocks Beach State Parks in North Carolina. This project, now in its fourth year, is a cooperative effort between the Soil Conservation Service, the North Carolina Division of State Parks, and the Horticultural Department of North Carolina State University at Raleigh. My special thanks are extended to my colleagues, Ray S. Pardue and Claude E. Crews, Park Superintendents; Lauris Joyner and Jesse O. Hines, Park Rangers; Bryon J. Taylor, Chief Park Naturalist; and Dr. Paul V. Nelson, Associate Professor, who is the horticultural plant nutritionist at the University.

I am also very grateful for the assistance of Dr. S. J. Dunn, Chairman, Department of Plant Science at the North Carolina Agricultural and Technical State University, who provided plants of several woody species for beach plantings and made a significant contribution in his selection work with marshhay cordgrass.

My thanks also go to Don Johnson, an artist friend of mine now living at Emerald Isle, North Carolina. He is responsible for the handsome line drawing of the windblown live oak on the cover.

The North Carolina Forest Service has been, through the years, extremely cooperative in furnishing seedlings of various trees which have been used in dune testing. All these past favors were appreciated.

The use of trade names in this publication does not imply endorsement by the Soil Conservation Service of the products named, nor criticism of similar ones not mentioned.

SECTION 1

THE BEACH ENVIRONMENT

The beach environment is hostile to plant life. Even native plants which have adapted themselves to seaside conditions through the ages find establishment difficult. For almost all of them, growth is slow. The inhibitive natural forces can be grouped under several headings:

SALT SPRAY

The plants growing along coastal beach areas are grouped together in what has been called "the salt spray community." A number of natural forces on the beach influence plant life, but by far the most potent factor is salt spray. Plants vary considerably in their resistance to its damaging effect. The most tolerant beach grasses and certain herbaceous plants are found closest to the ocean. Plants with less resistance to the salt spray and violent winds of frontal areas find their places toward the rear. Through the ages, they have arranged themselves in a definite pattern and in three very generalized zones: the "grass" or "pioneer" zone which is closest to the ocean and has the most direct exposure to the elements; a middle "scrub zone" which usually starts behind the protection of frontal dunes; and lastly and at the greatest distance from the ocean - the pine and hardwood or "forest zone" (Fig. 1). Through eons of time, certain plant species have become adapted to these varied site conditions. While there is always intergrading and over-lapping of plants between zones, many species stay relatively close within their prescribed areas. For example, seaoats, American beachgrass, and sea rocket will not prosper in the back areas among the trees - shrubs cannot move forward to the direct exposure of the frontal dune and heavy salt concentrations, nor can they back up into the shade of

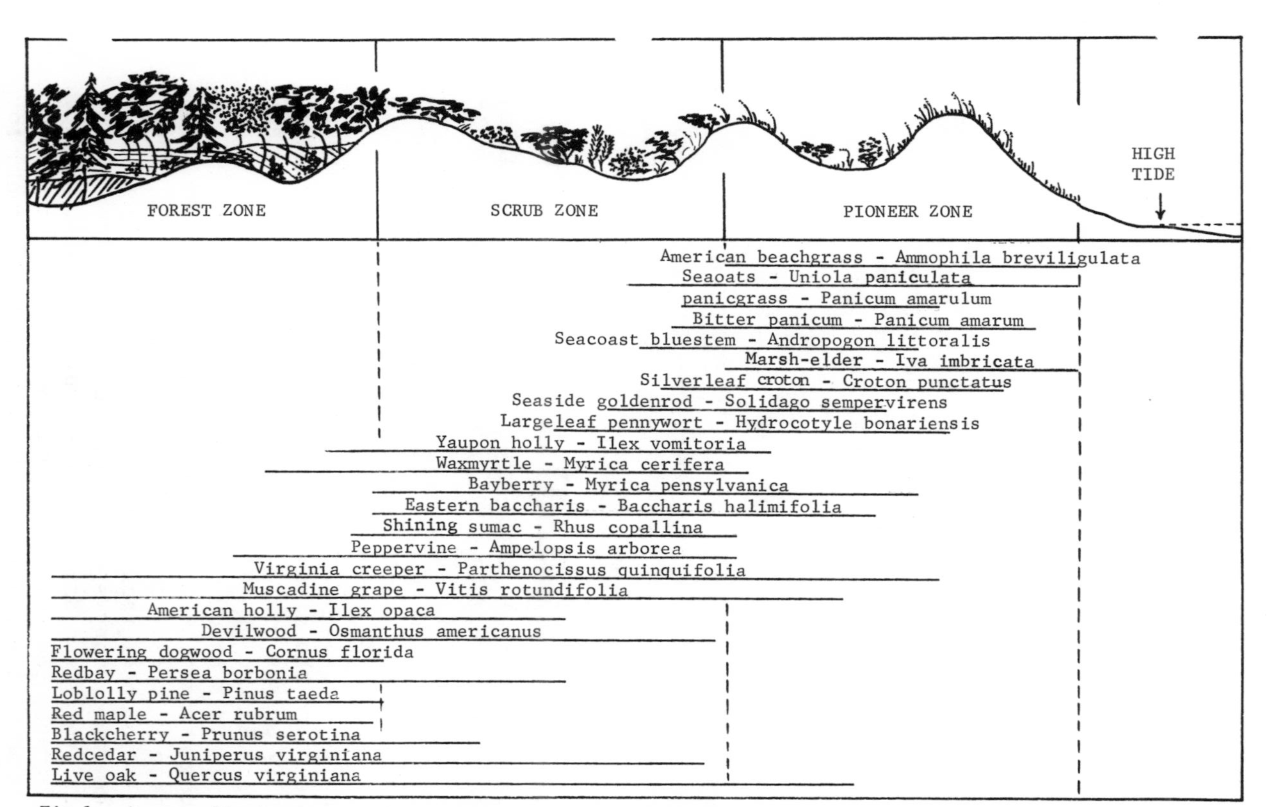

Fig 1 A generalized cross section of the beach area on Bogue Bank, North Carolina. Some common native plants with their zonal occurrence are included.

the forest zone. Trees which do advance into the scrub zone are whipped and sheared down to shrub size. The sprawling wind-flattened live oak is an outstanding example of this. Vines seem to have the widest zonal adaption. Peppervine, trumper creeper and coral honeysuckle are usually found in at least the two rearward zones; while summer grape, muscadine grape, and Virginia creeper may also be found "peering over" the crest of the frontal dune where, without support, they grow flat on the sand with the grass. Because of this wide zonal distribution and their good adaptation to seashore conditions, vines are very valuable for sand dune control work.

Salt-laden ocean winds can transform the majestic live oak into a wind sheared shrub, molded and smoothed into sculptured harmony with the contours of the rolling sand dunes (Fig. 2). This drastic influence of salt spray on plant

Fig. 2 A live oak molded by salt-laden sea winds. (Note dead twigs along upper surface.) Emerald Isle, North Carolina.

life was scientifically proven only a few years ago. Boyce (9) showed that the effervescence of bubbles of breaking waves ejected droplets of sea water into the air. As these are drifted inland by the wind, some of the water evaporates, thus, concentrating the salt in the droplets. On bright summer days, much of the ocean spray travels only a short distance before it evaporates completely. The resultant tiny salt crystals drift harmlessly to the ground. On the other hand, evaporation is retarded on cool, damp, cloudy days and during the night. This increases the inland drift and the amount of deposition on the vegetation.

The heaviest accumulation of spray occurs on the seaward side of vegetation. The chlorine ion enters the leaf tissue. These salts are not translocated, and when the concentration in the tissue becomes too great, the leaf or bud dies. Lack of translocation coupled with the differential deposition of spray (with the seaward leaves receiving the heaviest dose) causes the death of these most exposed leaves and twigs. Killing of the terminals causes profuse lateral branching and the development of a dense canopy in which individual leaves and twigs protect each other and do not accumulate killing amounts of salt. While this process is going on, the protected leeward stems of the plant grow and elongate in the direction away from the ocean. This is the reason for the picturesque windswept shrub and tree forms which are so characteristic of beach areas. When individual leaves and twigs form a canopy dense enough to protect the plant from lethal salt accumulations, so does the plant itself set up a barrier to help shield one or more plants behind it. These in turn shield others until a delicately balanced interrelationship is set up within the plant community. This does not mean that if the "number one" plant closest to the ocean is cut down that all others behind it will go down like a row of dominos. But the sudden removal of protective vegetation will usually cause injury or even kill the newly exposed plants. Beach landowners who open up new sites and bulldoze all the trees and brush, except for a few shade trees, find to their dismay that these trees soon show salt burn on the windward side where their protection has been removed. Eventually, many of them will die. Those with the least tolerance will go first (Fig. 3).

THE SAND

Dune sand performs the important job of providing a base to anchor and support the plant. This function is sometimes in jeopardy when gale winds swirl and sand begins to shift. Even so, sand does provide a medium in which plant roots may operate. Other that this, it has little to recommend it as a "soil" conducive to plant growth.

Fig. 3 Once thickly covered with shrubs and trees, this area was desolated by bulldozers west of Atlantic Beach, North Carolina. Most of the remaining live oak trees are dead or dying. Bogue Banks, North Carolina.

A number of sand samples taken in areas behind the frontal dune were analyzed. The two composite samples illustrated (Fig. 4) are generally representative of many of the beach areas in the Carolinas. They indicate a dearth of plant nutrients; a very high percentage of sand with only minute quantities of clay, silt, or organic matter; a good supply of calcium; and a basic pH value. A few of our beaches, or at least some sections of them, seem to be exempt from these dire conditions. For example, Sullivans Island, Folly Beach, and Hilton Head, all in South Carolina, have material which could reasonably be called a sandy soil in what we have designated as the scrub and forest zone.

The dune sand as characterized in Figure 4 has an extremely high percent of very fine sand. Once this dries out, as it easily does, it is difficult to wet again. Even after a drenching rain, one can go out in the dune area, scratch away the sand and in some places find it dry and powdery less than an inch from the surface. Gardeners have experienced this phenomenon when watering plants on dune sand. It is somewhat like trying to wet down a pile of talcum powder. This situation is partly due to the fine particle size, for in areas of coarse sand, water penetration is no problem. If this sand is

CHEMICAL AND PHYSICAL ANALYSIS OF REPLICATED SAND SAMPLES

FROM FT. MACON & HAMMOCKS BEACH STATE PARKS, NORTH CAROLINA

	FT. MACON	HAMMOCKS BEACH
Available Nutrients (ppm)		
NO_3 Nitrate (Nitrogen)	1	5
K Potassium	6	6
P Phosphorus	38	58
Ca Calcium	1600+	1600+
Mg Magnesium	26	19
Mn Manganese	2.4	2.4
pH	7.9	7.4
Organic Matter (%)	0.03	0.2
Sand (%)	99.86	99.80
Sand Particle Size (Millimeters)		
1 - 2 mm	1.02	1.40
0.5 - 1 mm	8.64	8.55
0.25 - 0.5 mm	35.56	31.75
0.1 - 0.25 mm	53.52	57.05
0.05 - 0.1 mm	1.12	1.05
Silt (%)	.062	.075
Clay (%)	.075	.125

Fig. 4

thoroughly washed in water, drained and dried, it readily absorbs water. Evidently, whatever causes the problem can be washed out. Initial tests by the Soils Department of North Carolina State University did not come up with a specific answer. They did note that the sand contained a noticeable amount of dissolvable salts which precipitated out upon evaporation. These salts were, however, readily dissolvable again. Slight crusting of the surface sand which is often found in the dunes may be due to salt concentration. The wetting problem seems to be tied in with the presence of these salts.

The depth of rain water percolation in dry dune sand within a given area varies from one spot to another. A hill of sand acts as a roof shedding water. Penetration of moisture at the crest is a thin layer which increases in depth down the sloping sides. At the bottom of the mound, the moisture finally filters into the sand where it and the capillary level of moisture from underneath may finally meet. This leaves a dry pocket of powdery sand under such a rise. Even in relatively flat dune valleys the depth of water penetration after a rain is very irregular. This must be caused by varying degrees of this unexplained inhibitive factor in the fine sand. Only a prolonged rain will finally soak the lingering dry spots. Though percolation is irregular over the surface, its downward movement is swift. During the summer, the upper horizon of sand - expecially the top three or four inches - begins to dry out minutes after a rain. After a week without rain, this layer becomes dry. These conditions can be a dangerous threat to the survival of new woody transplants. It is especially severe on young, shallow rooted plants which have come up from seed.

Yet, in the "subsoil" zone of dune land, there is more moisture than one would expect. When plants get their roots into this more constant supply of water they have overcome the first big obstacle to survival.

The almost pure sand profile of a dune offers little resistance to root penetration. This is beneficial. Most native dune plants develop deep and extensive root systems which tap the lower lying and more constant sources of water. This promotes plant survival and growth. The tough cuticle of leaves and their ability to roll inward to reduce transpiration are other factors which help many native beach plants to survive hot, dry summer periods.

TEMPERATURE

Did you ever walk barefoot on the bare sand among the dunes on a hot sunny day? Not for long you didn't! Sand temperatures were tested at Emerald Isle, North Carolina, in July 1970. On this particular day, the outside temperature in the shade was 97° F. The temperature of the bare sand surface in the dunes was 146° F., or a difference of 49°. One marvels at the resistance which enables native plants and especially the occasional seedlings of these plants to survive such heat. A beach plant sprung from a seed must surely be the result of a happy accident plus a combination of unusual circumstances!

In this same test, thermometer readings were also taken on the sand surface but under an inch of dead grass mulch which was dense enough to hide the sand. Here the temperature was 115° or 31° cooler than bare sand. The effect of mulch on the survival and growth of woody plants is discussed in a later chapter.

THE WIND

We have seen how the wind as a transporting agent of salt spray has the most profound effect on vegetation. Upon examination of the severity of salt spray damage along the coastline of the Carolinas, one finds considerable variation. On all South Carolina beaches, the influence was much more moderate than on the Outer Banks, Bogue Banks, and Brunswick County beaches of North Carolina. Plant species, both native and exotic, which can be found within 100 feet of the ocean on "The Grand Strand" (Fig. 5) are driven much further inland on these North Carolina beaches.

Fig. 5 Various trees and shrubs growing at the edge of the ocean protect garden plants in this Myrtle Beach, South Carolina, yard.

There is a logical explanation for this. Since salt deposition on vegetation is the most important controlling factor, then the difference must be due to the wind which not only affects surf conditions and the formation of salt water droplets but is also the agent for transporting the spray inland. The orientation of the coast or its directional position in relation to the ocean is of primary importance. South Carolina beaches run generally southwest to northeast or parallel with the prevailing southwest wind. Such a wind roughly paralleling the shore is more benign than one which blows across miles of open ocean and strikes the shoreline almost at right angles, as it does at the Brunswick County beaches of North Carolina and especially in the Bogue Banks area. Over the long haul, the southwest wind along South Carolina beaches and the North Carolina beaches in the Wilmington area produces a more moderate surf, carries less salt spray, and because of its long angle approach, is less liable to carry the spray as far inland.

The Outer Banks (from Cape Lookout northward) is a rugged area for plant life even though their position does not expose them to the southwest wind. The Nemesis of this segment of the coast is the fierce "nor'easter" especially prevalent during the winter. These blows are fairly frequent, kick up a tremendous surf and drive heavy concentrations of spray inland. Much of the damage to plants occurs here in the winter time. In contrast, the south-facing beaches in Brunswick and Carteret Counties in North Carolina literally have their backs to a northeast blow and ride them out with little difficulty.

Another wind factor to be reckoned with is its force and the resulting physical damage to plants. This is especially apparent in the banks area described above. But shredding of leaves can occur anywhere along the beach during hurricane winds and can be severe especially on introduced species. Native plants of the beach areas have growth characteristics which resist injury. Most of them (such as live oak, yaupon holly, yucca, devilwood, wax myrtle, and bayberry) have tough leathery leaves. In addition, such leaves are relatively small, often linear and, in general, shaped so that they present little surface to the wind. These same protective growth characteristics carry over to introduced species which are successfully used in beach landscaping. For example, six of the most popular landscaping plants - *Pittosporum tobira, Euonymus japonicus, Elaeagnus pungens, Raphiolepis umbellata, Ligustrum japonicum,* and *Yucca* sp. all have tough-skinned, leathery leaves. Leaves are often suspended on pliable petioles which will bend and allow the leaves to trail in the windstream. The palmetto and palm are good examples of this. And lastly, the branches and stems of many woody beach plants are very tough and resilient. People from Salter Path have related how they have seen the branches of trimmed live oaks thrashing the ground during a hurricane.

Other wind-caused injuries concern the movement of sand. Briefly, strong winds can sandblast, uproot, or bury plants. Most of this kind of action takes place in the pioneer zone. Plants usually found in this turbulent area have the ability to suffer through such periods of heavy winds and survive the damage.

SECTION 2

STILLING THE SAND WITH GRASSES AND FORBS

Along many of our coastal beaches the original vegetative cover of the sand dune areas has already been destroyed. In such places sand is on the move. It invades woodlands (Fig. 6), piles up against buildings, fills ditches,

Fig. 6 A moving dune burying a woodland area. Hammocks Beach State Park, North Carolina.

buries roads, lawns, and other installations, seeps into machinery, and in general is destructive and costly.

When the wind velocity reaches 12 to 15 miles per hour, it begins to pick up sand. The amount of material moved during a wind storm is amazing. In my own experience, a newly erected snow fence accumulated an 18-inch drift during a single wind storm - and the reverse - cement footings for a cottage laid 8 inches below the sand surface were partly exposed after one windy day.

Owners of property which is exposed to the wind should be extremely wary of destroying native cover. It should be removed only where absolutely necessary and then only after plans have been made to reestablish some kind of protective cover in its place. Mulches or topsoil, spread over the surface, may be used for quick protection until vegetation can be established.

Most of the problem areas of blowing sand occur in the pioneer zone. But denuded sites also occur in the more rearward zones. In all cases, the reestablishment of vegetation is usually begun with the planting of grass - the important first step on the road back to a "permanent" plant cover. These initial plantings improve soil moisture and plant nutrient conditions, moderate the sand temperatures and provide sand blast and salt spray protection for succeeding plants. Also the plant residues favor the increase of useful microorganisms in the sand. As the vegetation decays, plant nutrients are recycled back to the soil. This prepares the site for the introduction of the more permanent type plants.

When selecting a grass to vegetate barren areas it is important to use the species best adapted to the site conditions. Marshhay cordgrass *(Spartina patens)* is successful on the lower sand flats where droughtiness is not a problem. Coastal bermuda *(Cynodon dactylon)* is an excellent choice for disturbed areas such as dredged spoils or on sand soils with some "color." With a little care, both of these grasses will furnish long-lasting cover. Once these two species are established, it is usually not necessary to introduce other plants.

On the drier dune sites and where large quantities of sand are on the move, American beachgrass *(Ammophila breviligulata)* is by all odds the best choice even though it is more of a temporary sand stabilizer than a permanent sand fixer. After the sand has been secured, other native plants adapted to the zone begin to invade. This is the process of natural plant succession. It can be speeded by transplanting or seeding the more desirable species into the grass cover.

In the pioneer zone, and following American beachgrass, the three most important "permanent" grasses of the second phase are seaoats *(Uniola paniculata)*, bitter panicum *(Panicum amarum)*, and, to a lesser extent, marshhay cordgrass *(Spartina patens)*. There are other native grasses and forbs which are valuable but generally more difficult to plant and manage. However, all of them add to the total cover.

Where grass cover has been established in the scrub or forest zones, the transplanting of shrubs, vines, and trees which represent the climax species may be undertaken. This activity will be dealt with in a later chapter.

AMERICAN BEACHGRASS

AMMOPHILA BREVILIGULATA FERNALD

DESCRIPTION - This is a tough-leaved perennial grass 1 to 2 feet tall which spreads extensively from underground rhizomes (Fig. 7). Each seed stem has a single

Fig. 7 American beachgrass *(Ammophila breviligulata)* on top of the frontal dune. Hatteras Island, North Carolina.

spike or tail-like head 6 to 10 inches long. Seed production which is sparse in the mid and southern coastal areas of North Carolina improves considerably on the more northerly Outer Banks. The leaves remain partly green in the winter. This clearly distinguishes it from seaoats which dies back to the ground.

NOTES - American beachgrass, being extremely salt tolerant, thrives on dune sand and does best in the frontal areas where the sand is whipping and drifting around it. After a planting of beachgrass is dense enough to cut off sand movement, the plants lose vigor, and the stand begins to deteriorate. This is particularly true of beachgrass south of Cape Hatteras. At this stage an adequate grass cover can be maintained only with applications of fertilizer. This is the reason American beachgrass plantings are regarded as a preparatory measure rather than a final vegetative solution.

American beachgrass is well adapted to our coastal dunes in the northern or Bodie Island area of the Outer Banks of North Carolina. South of here, its adaptability slowly decreases and its production of seedheads declines sharply. Even at Atlantic Beach, North Carolina, seedheads are scarce.

No specific effort has been made to determine the southernmost natural occurance of American beachgrass. There are several colonies of it at Ocean Isle Beach, North Carolina. Very likely its natural occurance "feathers out" somewhere in the vicinity of the South Carolina line. This, however, does not preclude its usefulness in South Carolina. Three South Carolina Soil Conservation Service test plantings on Bull Island, on a beach site near Georgetown and in the vicinity of Charleston prove that it is a useful sandbinder in these latitudes. A large planting established in 1970 on Hilton Head Island, South Carolina, seems to be doing well, but more time is needed to make a final evaluation.

The necessity for protecting the unstable sands of our eastern coastal region was recognized many years ago. In fact, the Federal Government appropriated money during the period 1826 to 1839 for setting out American beachgrass near the "Village" of Provincetown, Rhode Island.

In recent times, American beachgrass was planted extensively in the Bodie Island area of the Outer Banks by the Civilian Conservation Corps. This work took place during the period 1934 to 1936. Stock was secured by digging and dividing native plants.

In modern times, the series of hurricanes, beginning with "Hazel" in 1954, aroused new interest in dune erosion control. The National Park Service and the Soil Conservation Service began testing various species of grasses on the Outer Banks in the late 50's. In 1962, North Carolina State University scientists joined in the work after funds had been provided by the North Carolina State Legislature. This gave great impetus to the program.

In the spring of 1963, the first commercial production of American beachgrass was begun in North Carolina. Planting stock was furnished by the Soil Conservation Service from its National Plant Materials Center, Beltsville, Maryland. An acre was set out at the North Carolina State Forestry Division nursery at Clayton, North Carolina (Fig. 8). Another increase block was established at the Coastal Stabilization Nursery, New Bern, North Carolina. All of this stock originated from a Soil Conservation Service collection from Lewes, Delaware. During the next seven years, these two nurseries produced millions of plants which amply satisfied the needs in the Carolinas. Since that time, the state nursery has ceased production of the grass. However, Spake's Nursery, Manteo, North Carolina, has recently gone into production to provide a new source at the northern end of the Outer Banks area.

A new and more vigorous selection called 'Hatteras' was selected at the Clayton Nursery from the original 'Lewes.' It was released in 1970 by the North Carolina State

Fig. 8 First production of American beachgrass *(Ammophila breviligulata)* in North Carolina. North Carolina Division of Forestry Nursery, Clayton, North Carolina, July 1963.

University Experiment Station and is now in commercial production. This new strain may be superior especially in areas subject to heavy sand depositions. The old commercial Lewes has, however, given satisfactory results. Both are being tested along with a third strain called 'Cape' (Fig. 9). This one was developed by the Soil Conservation Service Plant Materials Center at Cape May Court House, New Jersey. The original selection was

Fig. 9 Test plots of American beachgrass selections. 'Cape' in foreground. Hammocks Beach State Park, North Carolina.

found in a natural stand at Cape Cod, Massachusetts. It is a very vigorous coarse-bladed type which is now being certified in New Jersey. Test plots on the New Jersey dunes resulted in "no significant difference" in weight of herbage produced by the two new selections. Unmeasured observations of all three at Hammocks Beach State Park in North Carolina seemed to be slightly in favor of Cape, with both the new strains more vigorous than Lewes. The stems of Hatteras are finer and more numerous than those of the more robust Cape.

PLANTING - At the nursery, clumps of American beachgrass are dug and divided into separate plants with one to three or more stems each (Fig. 10). Plantings must be put in during the cool season - approximately from November 1 to March 30. Plantings are usually made by hand. However, on large scale jobs, crawler tractors pulling converted tobacco planters are used. The National Park

Fig. 10 The sharpshooter spade and seven American beachgrass plants ready for planting. The bunch of grass at left will make seven or eight more plants.

Service people have planted miles of beach in this manner on the dunes of the Cape Hatteras National Seashore Recreational Area.

For hand planting, a "sharpshooter" or a nursery spade is a good tool for the job. Another implement which works well if the sand is moist is a wood splitting wedge welded as an extension to a 3 foot length of pipe.

The grass stems are planted upright in the sand and about 8 inches deep. Part of the leaf surface may be buried. The leaves are not trimmed before planting. With hand planting, each plant must be firmly packed with the heel of the foot. Care must be taken to keep the roots moist during the planting operation. The spacing of plants need not be exact. Rows with 2 or 2 1/2 foot middles and with plants 1 to 1 1/2 feet apart in the row would include most of the average plantings. At the 1 by 2 foot spacing 1,000 plants will cover 2,000 square feet, and 3,750 square feet if the 1 1/2 by 2 1/2 foot rate is used. The closer spacing is used when planting critical situations where there is considerable wind and sand movement. These densities, if properly fertilized, will still the sand in the second season. As the space between plants is widened, the length of time to establish complete cover is increased. But this disadvantage can be largely overcome by a good program of fertilization. Wide spacings to something like 4 foot rows with plants 2 feet apart in the row have been tried with success. This is feasible in back areas where sand movement is not too great, where the speed of gaining cover is not crucial, or where labor is difficult to secure.

Beachgrass may be used to build dunes. These are usually laid off parallel to the ocean. Along the ocean front, large quantities of sand are on the move. In this situation a snow fence placed along the line of the proposed dune will speed up the accumulation. When the sand nears the top of the fence the newly formed dune is planted in long parallel rows. This method has also been successfully applied to patching breaks in established dune lines. Whether the fencing is used or not, the parallel rows of grass should be set about 2 feet apart. To prevent most of the sand from being trapped by the rows at the outside edges of the proposed dune, the plant spacings of the outer rows are increased. To illustrate - all row middles might be set at 2 feet. In the four to six rows at the central ridge of the dune, the plants are placed 1 foot apart. Then working outward on both sides of these center rows, the plant spacings are increased as rows are added. A 4-foot plant spacing in the two outer rows is the maximum spread needed. Plant density may also be regulated by changing the width of middles. This kind of planting pattern will allow the sand to drift into the dune site. For a year or two, the greatest accumulation of sand will occur along the center line in the denser stand of grass.

FERTILIZATION - The use of fertilizer is the key to the successful establishment of American beachgrass. Nitrogen is the most important element. On beach sands, the grass shows very limited response to phosphate and almost none to potash. The ideal fertilizer ratio is a 30-10-0 (Nitrogen, Phosphate, Potash) analysis which is sometimes available in the Nags Head and Manteo, North Carolina, area. Most cottagers will have to rely on standard commercial grades such as 10-10-10 or 8-8-8, or, even better, the 16-8-8 lawn mixture.

RECOMMENDED FERTILIZER RATES

BROADCAST PER 1,000 SQUARE FEET

TYPE FERTILIZER	TIME OF APPLICATION		
FIRST YEAR	MARCH	JUNE	SEPT.
(1) 30-10-0	4 lbs.	3 lbs.	3 lbs.
or			
(2) 16-8-8	6 lbs.	6 lbs.	6 lbs.
or			
(3) 10-10-10	10 lbs.	10 lbs.*	10 lbs.*
or			
(4) 8-8-8	12 lbs.	12 lbs.*	12 lbs.*
SECOND YEAR			Only If Needed
(5) 30-10-0	3 lbs.	0	2 lbs.
or			
(6) 16-8-8	6 lbs.	0	4 lbs.
or			
(7) 10-10-10	10 lbs.	0	5 lbs.**
or			
(8) 8-8-8	12 lbs.	0	6 lbs.**

* In fertilizer schedules No. 3 and 4, the June and September application may be changed to 3 lbs. of ammonium nitrate

**In fertilizer schedules No. 7 and 8, the September applications may be changed to 2 lbs. of ammonium nitrate

In future years, maintenance includes the use of second year spring fertilizer rates with adjustments made to maintain healthy, <u>but not luxuriant</u>, growth. The fall application will usually not be needed. Over-fertilization produces dense decaying masses of dead vegetation. This sets up a situation favorable for disease organisms and other adverse conditions which can thin out or kill the grass. On some sites, beachgrass may not require fertilizer every year. The ideal condition is to maintain a fairly open stand with about two-thirds to three-fourths of the sand surface under vegetative cover.

SEAOATS

UNIOLA PANICULATA L.

DESCRIPTION - Along the coast from Cape Henry, Virginia, into Texas the perennial seaoats is the predominant dune grass. The leaves are pale green, tough and resemble those of American beachgrass. They do, however, die back to the ground each winter. Beachgrass remains partially green. The seed heads of compressed spikelets mature in September and are borne at the ends of stiff stems 3 or more feet in length. Individual seeds somewhat resemble the common oats of agronomic use. Most of them are empty "pops." Each spikelet of 20 or so seeds will usually contain only a few viable ones. The plant spreads from long extended rhizomes. These are relatively few in number and almost as coarse as the above ground stems. The nodes which are the growing points on both stems and rhizomes are often a foot or more apart.

NOTES - Within its range, seaoats is the most important species in the pioneer zone. Fortunately, it is a plant of great beauty. It contributes a superb sixth "s" to the beachscape combination of sea, surf, sand, sun, and sky.

Like American beachgrass, it flourishes best where sand is drifting and accumulating. Unlike beachgrass, it persists as a perennial cover after the sand has been stilled (Fig. 11). It is the perfect replacement for American beachgrass in pioneer zone plantings.

Seaoats stems root readily at the nodes. This enables it to keep ahead of drifting sand. Occasional plants which take root in bare frontal areas immediately begin to trap large quantities of sand. This forces excessive top growth at the expense of lateral increase. Low mounds are built. As they steepen, the unprotected sides become unstable. Wind erosion carves the slopes until abrupt hummocks are formed. Such formations are not desirable for controlling beach erosion. For this reason, the slower growing seaoats is most often interplanted with or introduced into stands of less persistent plants, usually American beachgrass. As the beachgrass fades, the seaoats slowly takes over to provide the long lasting

Fig. 11 Seaoats *(Uniola paniculata)* in a complete stand on a frontal dune, Fort Fisher, North Carolina.

cover. In this manner, the formation of hummocks is avoided.

SEEDING - Seaoats spikelets are ripe and may be stripped in late September. They are collected as soon as ripe to avoid loss to birds and normal shattering. If seed is planted 2 to 3 inches deep in dune sand during the winter, they will sprout in the spring. Germination is not high, but stands are usually adequate. However, during the first hot, dry spells, seedlings begin to die. This continues through the early summer until, in my experience, less than 3 percent remain in the fall. Plant stress due to the simple lack of moisture may be greatly magnified by an increasing concentration of salt near the surface of the sand as moisture wicks upward and evaporates.

On the dunes, the natural volunteering of seaoats from seed is very limited and irregular from year to year. Usually, it is difficult to find even a single seedling. But there are times and places where a very thin sprinkling of new plants can be found. This must be the result of a certain set of site and weather conditions which cover and protect the seed until germination, and then favor the survival of the new plant. It has been noted that volunteering is apt to be more usual in the exposed frontal areas (and even at the seaside base of the first dune) than in areas behind the first dune. The accumulation of vegetative trash, seaweed, etc. - even the wheel tracks of beach buggies - probably helps to promote volunteering.

Only one of our five beach seedings was moderately successful. This was a row planting in a sand flat where moisture was quite close to the surface. This indicates that the supply of moisture is certainly one of the controlling factors. Dune seedings might be pulled through with frequent waterings, shading, or both. On the other hand, seedings at inland nurseries on fertile soil and watered as needed have not done much better. It is thought that in this situation the young plants fall prey to various soil-borne fungi or other disease organisms.

A new autumn planting seemed to offer hope. Seed of the 1971 crop were held dry over winter. In April 1972, they were mixed with moist peat moss, placed in a plastic bag, and held in a refrigerator through the summer. On September 3, 1972, the seed was removed from refrigeration. The whole batch - moss and all - was planted in rows 2 1/2 inches deep and watered. Two weeks later, a good stand (nine plants per foot) of vigorous looking seedlings was up. It was hoped that the cooler days of autumn would favor seedling growth to the point where they might survive the winter. But this was not to be. Suddenly, over a one week period in late October, all seedlings died. This small disaster looked more like the influence of chemical rather than biological factors.

PLANTING ROOTSTOCK - Until these problems are solved, the establishment of seaoats on our beaches will have to depend on digging and dividing native plants. The digging of seaoats or the cutting of its seed heads is illegal in both the Carolinas. So when planting stock is needed, the cottager will have to get along with what he can beg from a friend or dig on his own place. In North Carolina, permission to gather seaoats may be had from the local County Dune Protection Officer. These plants are dug as deeply as possible in order to get a portion of the rhizome with each plant. When replanting, the stock is set at least a foot in depth and packed in tightly. This means that at least the basal part of the leaves will be buried. A watering at planting time will help. To emphasize - the secret in planting seaoats is deep planting.

Seaoats may be introduced into the row middles of American beachgrass plantings. A sparse planting rate of 4 x 4 to 8 x 8 foot intervals will finally get the job done. A good time for this work is early spring - at the beginning of the first or second season for the beachgrass. Of course, seaoats may be planted by itself in the more protected areas where sand accumulation in hummocks is not a problem.

When the problem of nursery production is solved, the improved quantity and quality of planting stock may enable us to plant it right along with the beachgrass and increase the planting rates for other work.

FERTILIZATION - The first and second year fertilizer recommendations for American beachgrass will also do for seaoats. This grass responds to fertility. But after the first season, great care must be taken not to over fertilize. Two cottagers at Emerald Isle, North Carolina, used large amounts of fertilizer on their seaoats. One year of "the tallest seaoats on the Atlantic Coast," was followed by an almost complete die out the next spring. The sudden upward shift in fertility and opening up of the grass stand promoted the invasion of broad-leaved weeds principally the rough-leaved, yellow-flowered camphorweed *(Heterotheca subaxillaris)*.

The winter die out is associated with the heavy accumulation of dead plant residue. This condition sets up a dark, damp environment which favors growth of disease organisms. Also, harmful acids may result from the decomposition. A number of grasses are subject to this trouble. Removal of the excess herbage in the fall will solve this problem. This practice is often impractical. Furthermore, on the beach the removal of any kind of protective vegetation is just not mentioned in the better circles of seaside gardeners!

BITTER PANICUM

PANICUM AMARUM ELL.

DESCRIPTION - Bitter panicum is an important perennial of the frontal dune areas (Fig. 12). The stands are rather open. The leaves are smooth without hair, bluish in color, 1/4 to 1/2 inch wide and 4 to 12 inches long. The seed heads are narrow, compressed and most often sparsely seeded. It has been determined by the North Carolina State University Botany Department that this species is a

Fig. 12 Bitter panicum *(Panicum amarum)* - the low, widely spreading type, on a dune slope. Kitty Hawk, North Carolina.

sterile triploid. No viable seed are produced. A very agressive but scattered system of far reaching rhizomes allows the plant to spread widely.

Another form of this species is a much more robust type (Fig. 13). The stems and leaves are much coarser than the above. Seed stalks ascend from the sand in an arc, and the seed heads are wider, longer, and more heavily seeded. The seed are not viable. It spreads slowly from short, heavy rhizomes (almost tillers) to form open clumps. The leaves and stems are smooth and bluish as above.

NOTES - The low growing, wide spreading type of bitter panicgrass (the first one above) is the most useful of the two described. It is perfectly adapted in the pioneer zone and will also occupy open areas in the scrub zone. The lack of density as a ground cover is partly overcome by its tenacity as a perennial and its widely spreading habit. These traits are put to good advantage by using this species as one of several to follow American beachgrass. A "sprinkling of sprigs" at widely spaced intervals will spread unobtrusively until it is suddenly discovered as an important element of the total cover.

Fig. 13 Bitter panicum (*Panicum amarum*). This robust form is not as useful as the low spreading one. Seaoats are in the background. Emerald Isle, North Carolina.

PLANTING - Since viable seed are not produced, all increases must be made by using rootstock found in the wild. Planting stock consists of a stem with part of the rhizome attached or 8 to 12 inch lengths of the rhizome without the above ground parts. At least two nodes must be present on each piece. The root parts are planted 4 inches deep. Since planting stock is not readily available, a wide spaced interval of 4 to 8 feet seems most practical. Like seaoats, it should be planted in early spring.

FERTILIZATION - The first year individual plants are fertilized after new growth is evident in late spring. A rounded teaspoon of 8-8-8 or 10-10-10 broadcast in a one foot circle around each plant will help. After this, the normal fertilization maintenance schedule as for American beachgrass is sufficient.

MARSHHAY CORDGRASS

SPARTINA PATENS (AIT.) MUHL.

DESCRIPTION - This perennial is a widespread inhabitant of the sand flats and moist areas (Fig. 14). The stems are slender and up to 2 to 2 1/2 feet tall. Seed heads are composed of two to several compressed spikes from a central axis. A comparatively good crop of viable seed is produced in early September. The leaves are rolled inward giving them a rush-like appearance. They are mostly less than 1/8 inch wide. The grass spreads to make dense stands by means of a network of slender rhizomes which are often banded with purple.

Fig. 14 Marshhay cordgrass *(Spartina patens)* on a sand flat north of Corolla, North Carolina. J. B. Hungerford, State Resource Conservationist, Raleigh, North Carolina.

NOTES - While this species prefers moist sites, it will also produce and hold a scattered stand in drier sites such as hammocks between dunes (Fig. 15). This capability coupled with its perennial persistence gives it a worthwhile value as a component - one of several species which together will provide the final long-lasting dune protection. It is adapted in any one of the three beach zones. Its most important use is for revegetating barren moist flats, spoil, ditch, and channel banks. In such places, it can be expected to get the job done without long delay.

On September 12, 1966, Pea Island Refuge personnel (Department of Interior) collected 26 pounds of the clipped off seed heads. This lot threshed out 1 pound, 12 ounces of clean seed. Some of this seed was used the following

Fig. 15 Marshhay cordgrass in a dune valley. Note seed heads.

spring to establish successful stands of marshhay cordgrass on sandy "nesting bar" sites. These areas were very moist. Seed was mixed with 8-8-8 fertilizer in pellet form and planted in rows with a single row fertilizer distributor. Planting depth was about 1 1/2 inches. The date was February 10, 1967. In this test, the 1966 seed stored dry since collection, germinated about ten days later than a second lot which had been stratified in cold, damp peat moss for three weeks prior to planting. Both lots produced satisfactory stands which averaged three to five seedlings per foot of row.

Spaced plantings of individual plants derived from the above seed were made at North Carolina A & T State University in 1967. There was a surprising lack of uniformity in the growth characteristics of these specimens. Some were dense, some open; there were tall and short ones, good spreaders and seeders, and also poor ones.

The wide range of conservation uses for this plant, plus its production of viable and apparently harvestable seed crops, gives this plant a high use potential. Collections from the southeastern Atlantic and the Gulf Coasts have been underway since 1971. These are being sent to the Soil Conservation Service plant materials centers at Americus, Georgia, and Cape May Court House, New Jersey, and North Carolina A & T State University. The selection of plants which have the needed requirements for conservation work will be made at these stations.

PLANTING - Plantings are made in late winter and early spring. Rootstock is easy to locate in lower lying areas such as one commonly finds along the sounds or Intracoastal Waterway. The use of seed is still not practical until the Soil Conservation Service completes its work on selections which can be readily harvested.

Planting stock consists of several stems rooted at the base and preferably with a section of rhizome attached. In vegetating sand flats, spoils, etc., the stock is planted in 3 to 4 foot rows with plants 2 to 4 feet apart in the row. Depth of planting is about 4 inches. In introducing this species into the drier dune valleys, wider spacings can be used and the depth of planting increased to 5 inches or more.

FERTILIZATION - In large-scale rootstock plantings on sand flats use first year broadcast fertilizer as on American beachgrass. Individual plants widely spaced in dune valleys should each be treated with a rounded teaspoon of complete fertilizer after spring growth starts.

OTHER NATIVE GRASSES

The following grasses are useful perennials. All of them but one (seashore saltgrass) will add materially to the permanent maintenance-free cover in the pioneer zone on the dunes. Their natural occurrence as they begin to appear in sand stilled areas should be recognized and their value appreciated. Neither rootstock nor seed of these is available commercially. Only bitter panicgrass (below) is at present produced in small quantities by Soil Conservation Service plant material centers.

PANICGRASS (*PANICUM AMARULUM* HITCHC. AND CHASE) is a rather dense upright bunchgrass 3 to 4 feet tall (Fig. 16). The stems are coarse, straight, and stiff. The leaves and stems are bluish in color. The seed head is partially compressed. A moderate amount of viable seed is produced each fall. The crown of the plant enlarges slowly from short almost vertical tillers.

This grass occurs in scattered clumps in dune areas. Strangely, its range includes New Jersey to the northern area of the Outer Banks, but then skips all the way down to Florida and the beaches of the Gulf Coast.

A selection (BN-8360) found by the Soil Conservation Service at Back Bay, Virginia, has been increased at the Beltsville National Plant Materials Center. It has been seeded inland with success. A test planting at Orangeburg, South Carolina, did well. But at the beach, direct seeding results on the dunes have been poor. A 1960 planting on Bodie Island, North Carolina, put in by the National Park Service personnel was partially successful with about three plants per square yard. Rod rows at Fort Macon, North Carolina, in 1970 germinated but the seedlings disappeared during the summer. Another seeding on a moist sand flat germinated and grew vigorously. This work was done by the U. S. Fish and Wildlife Service at the Pea Island National Wildlife Refuge in 1969. The results show much promise for direct seedings on this type of site and dredged spoils.

Fig. 16 Clumps of *Panicum amarulum* on the Outer Banks near Corolla, North Carolina. Penny Hill, a moving dune, in background.

At present, a seaside gardener's best bet is to dig and divide clumps. These planted a foot apart in rows will make attractive plant borders or the leading edge of salt wind barriers.

SEACOAST BLUESTEM (*ANDROPOGON LITTORALIS* NASH) grows 1 to 1 1/2 feet tall (Fig. 17). The stems are at first reclining and flattened in cross section with the lower leaf sheaths overlapping. The seed stems are slender,

Fig. 17 Seacoast bluestem (*Andropogon littoralis*). Plant with feathery seed heads almost mature. Bogue Banks, North Carolina.

upright, and copiously covered with short, silvery hair (awns) when the seeds are ripe. A low fall sun slanting across stands of this grass might remind one of a frosted fairyland. It must be regarded as a bunchgrass although the clumps increase slowly in size. It is well adapted to the dunes but is always in open stands with areas of bare sand between clumps. This bluestem, so named because the stems are chalky-blue, is found in quantity on Bogue Banks, North Carolina, and just south of Duck, North Carolina. It is scarce north of here until it again appears in New Jersey, Delaware, and Staten Island, New York.

The ripe seed heads may be gathered and broadcast over areas already stabilized. Chopping the stems into the sand will help to secure volunteers. On Bogue Banks, nature is doing the job without assistance. Each year the grass has increased visibly by the natural spread of its windblown seed.

LONGAWN VIRGINIA WILDRYE (*ELYMUS VIRGINICUS* L. VAR. *GLABRIFLORUS* VASEY) is a cool season perennial. It has a preference for moist areas but is found quite often in dune valleys (Fig. 18). After a summer rest period, the

Fig. 18 Longawn Virginia wildrye (*Elymus virginicus* var. *glabriflorus*) on dune sand with yucca. Cherry Grove Beach, South Carolina.

grass begins regrowth in the fall, reaches full flush in the spring, and goes to seed in July. The seed heads resemble those of rye grain. The seed, which have long bristly awns remain on the stems for a month or more after ripening. They are viable and have good germinating vigor. Successful seedings on moist sites have been made. Similar trials were established in dune valleys on September 16, 1972. The first sprouts were noticed on October 23rd. The green winter leaves may also be useful as a grazing plant for geese.

HAIRAWN MUHLY (*MUHLENBERGIA CAPILLARIS* LAM.) is strictly a bunchgrass - erect to almost 3 feet but usually closer to 2 (Fig. 19). The seed heads are one-third to one-half the entire height of the stems. The fine seeds with their long purple, hair-like attachments wave in the wind. The slender, upright stems and the partly rolled leaves form dense clumps. In North Carolina the grass is common on Bodie and Hatteras Islands. In South Carolina it is found at Hilton Head and on some of the islands off the coast at Charleston.

Fig. 19 Hairawn muhly (*Muhlenbergia capillaris*). Atlantic Beach, North Carolina.

Hair muhley is most often found in the dune valleys and flats where the sand has more moisture. Its dense, upright habit of growth has wind stilling qualities. The fine purple haze of its top has considerable decorative value. It should be excellent for borders or first line rows in salt wind barrier plantings.

The plant is propagated by dividing the clumps in early spring before growth.

SEASHORE PASPALUM (*PASPALUM VAGINATUM* SWARTZ) is not a resident of dry dune land (Fig. 20, 21). Its favorite habitat is along shorelines on coastal sounds, road shoulders, and other moist, sandy areas near the coast. This low creeping grass resembles bermudagrass but the small "v" shaped seed head gives it away. It is closely related to bahiagrass and dallisgrass. It spreads by runners as well as underground rhizomes. The seed stems are usually less than a foot in height. Where mowed they may be only an inch or two tall. The leaves taper to a partially rolled tip. When mowed the grass makes a very dense, flat sod.

Seashore paspalum endures on very wet sites. Even saltwater tides which flood it daily have no detrimental effect. Its principal use is for lawns which may extend down to the water and beyond the high tide mark. It is propagated by transplanting the runners or rhizomes.

Fig. 20 Seashore paspalum (*Paspalum vaginatum*). Kitty Hawk, North Carolina.

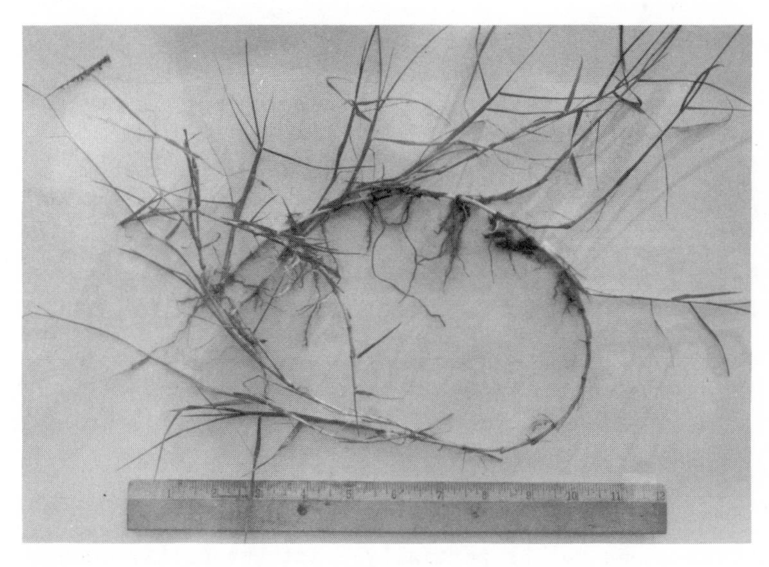

Fig. 21 A runner of seashore paspalum.

USEFUL SAND DUNE FORBS

There are a number of useful forbs which are native to sand dune areas. If seed sources are nearby, they will tend to invade areas which are being held by grass. Others may be started by transplanting or sowing seed. Many of them are valuable in that they add variety, interest, and effectiveness to the dune cover. A few of the more important ones are mentioned below:

LARGELEAF PENNYWORT (*HYDROCOTYLE BONARIENSIS* LAM.) is one of the easiest to transplant. A few dozen sprigs will spread quickly, infiltrate the grass, and cover a large area in a few years. (Also see Page 194)

LIPPIA [*LIPPIA NODIFLORA* (L.) MICHAUX] is a low viney ground cover which roots at the nodes. It prefers the flat areas where moisture is near the surface. Growth and spread is fast. The rooted runners are used for increase. (Also see Page 199)

DAYFLOWER (*COMMELINA ERECTA* L.) endures the sand dune environment without trouble even though it looks out of place (Fig. 22). It is a close relative of wandering

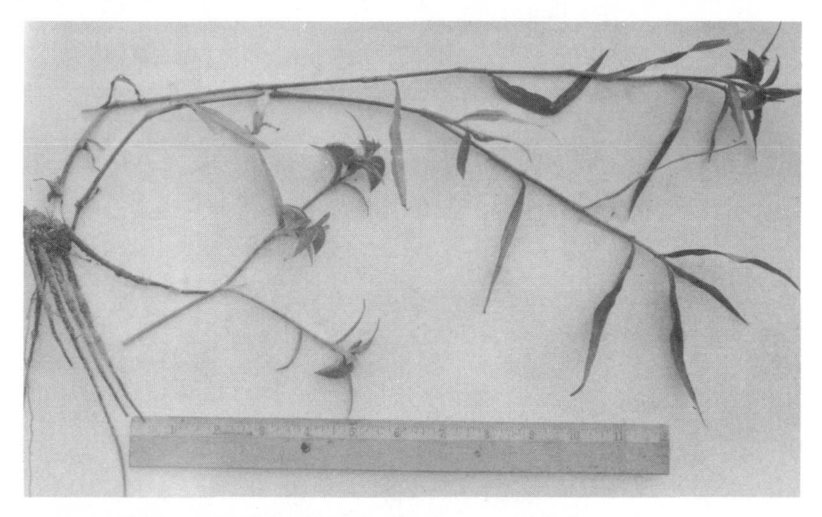

Fig. 22 Dayflower (*Commelina erecta*). Emerald Isle, North Carolina

Jew. The stems may be partially erect but mostly decumbent, fleshy, and 2 to 3 feet long. They arise from a cluster of thickened dark-brown roots. The flowers are light blue. The leaves are light green, lance shaped, pointed, with the lower part forming a sheath around the stem. This perennial is propagated by division and by summer cuttings.

SEASIDE GOLDENROD (*SOLIDAGO SEMPERVIRENS* L.) may be found along the coast in saline sands from Virginia to Florida (Fig. 23). The basal stem leaves are up to 8 inches long and 1/2 to 1 1/2 inches wide. Near the top of the stems, they are drastically reduced in size to less than an inch in length. Stems arise from short, stocky rhizomes and are usually unbranched. The showy heads of bright yellow

Fig. 23 Seaside goldenrod (*Solidago sempervirens*). Holden Beach, North Carolina.

flowers appear in October. The beauty of this plant lies partly in the healthy appearance of its lush bright green leaves which seems to belie its austere environment. This perennial may be propagated by separating the short, stocky rhizomes.

TRAILING WILDBEAN [*STROPHOSTYLES HELVOLA* (L.) ELL.] an annual trailing legume, is another plant which catches ones attention with its "exhuberant" growth on the dunes (Fig. 24). Seed germinate in the spring and growth is slow at first. Toward midsummer, the prostrate, twining vines make their move. Sometimes entire dunes are covered with a green mat. Each leaf has three lobed leaflets. The typical bean type flowers, which are rose-lavender in

Fig. 24 Trailing wildbean (*Strophostyles helvola*). Emerald Isle, North Carolina.

color, are born at the tips of single elongated stalks. One to three or more beans per stalk ripen in mid September and October. Heavy seed crops are common. The fuzzy coated beans are eaten by quail, doves, and rabbits. The humus and nitrogen that this legume adds to the soil is probably of significant benefit to many companion perennial plants. The smothering effect of its dense growth on other native vegetation has not been evaluated. Since it comes so late in the season, it cannot be very harmful.

Wildbean may be introduced by planting the seeds in the dune sand anytime during the dormant season. The beans should be covered 1 to 2 inches deep. They may not show up well the first season. This may be due to a lack of bacterial inoculation on the roots. Later, this deficiency seems to right itself.

SILVER-LEAF CROTON (*CROTON PUNCTATUS* IACQ.) is an annual or short-lived perennial (Fig. 25). It grows 1 to 2 feet tall. The entire plant is pubescent. The leaves, especially the undersides, are silvery. The stems are tan, dusted with cinnamon. Leaves are oval to long-oval in form and up to 2 1/2 inches long. Small clusters of blooms appear in late July through August at the densely velvety twig ends. Glossy gray seed with darker mottlings ripen in October through November. Once started, these plants reseed freely. The seed are valuable as choice quail, dove, and cardinal food. The plant can be propagated by planting the seed during the late fall and up to mid-March. They are covered 1 to 1 1/2 inches deep in dune sand.

Fig. 25 Silver-leaf croton (*Croton punctatus*). Isle of Palms, South Carolina.

SECTION 3

WOODY PLANTINGS FOR DUNE PROTECTION

The vegetative protection of dune land from erosion differs from inland standards. Soil erosion by water is by far the greatest hazard on the clays and other fine textured soils of the Piedmont. At the beach, such erosion takes place only where water is concentrated in the runoff from roads, roofs, topsoiled yards, or other impervious surfaces. On the undisturbed sand dunes, water intake is so rapid that there is no runoff. Instead, wind is the prime sand mover. A good tight sod will give complete protection on any soil type, but at the beach the height of vegetation is an additional favorable factor. Standing plants will diminish the force of the wind. So when evaluating dune protection, cover density is supplemented by height. Woody plantings, as they grow out and above the grass, will add a potent stabilizing effect.

The past ten years have seen much activity in the nursery production of American beachgrass and its establishment for sand dune erosion control along the coast. As these plantings matured, the supply of sand drifting into them was shut off. This caused the grass to thin out and deteriorate. To maintain the stands, it was necessary to apply fertilizer. This was no great problem for the average beach lot owner. But it was a different story for the National Park Service people who had planted many miles of beachgrass along the Cape Hatteras National Seashore. Helicopter applications of fertilizer proved to be effective but very expensive.

The most logical solution to this problem is to promote the increase of long-lived native plants in the fading American beachgrass. As long as the area is stable, these natives will begin to invade naturally. Some may have been present in remnant quantities when the beachgrass was first planted. Nature may be assisted by introducing them by over-seeding or transplanting. Moderate amounts of fertilizer will encourage this take-over.

Any plants which are to be introduced in the pioneer zone should be adapted to that zone. These would be the tough herbaceous species - mostly grasses, several forbs, and most important of all, seaoats. In the scrub and forest zones, the introduction of shrubs, vines, and trees would be appropriate. Stoesz and Brown (5) had this to say about plant selection: "The establishment of permanent vegetation is the final objective in the stabilization of dunes. The climax species of plants ... in the area are best for the purpose. If woody plants are the climax, the adapted species of trees and shrubs properly managed will provide the best permanent cover ... and should therefore be considered for plantings." Some of the hardier shrubs such as northern bayberry and eastern baccharis and vines such as wild bamboo and Virginia creeper may be moved into the pioneer zone in the lee of the first dune. Both of the vines will grow up the back slope to the top of the frontal dune. But no matter where transplants are to be put, the area must first be stabilized with grass. American beachgrass takes about two years to provide sufficient protection. Sometimes, one year will suffice where exceptional growth is made.

In the fall of 1969, woody plant studies were begun to: (1) determine which species were best suited; and (2) to determine the cultural practices required to establish them. This is a study with the Soil Conservation Service, North Carolina State Parks Division, and the Horticultural Department of North Carolina State University cooperating. The work is set up at two sites - Fort Macon and Hammocks Beach State Parks (Fig. 26).

The notes in this chapter which concern sand dune plantings are drawn from our work with these plots and partly from experience with plantings at my cottage and those of other seaside gardeners. One must remember that in nature most of these same plants may take many years to develop to any appreciable size. The plantsman must adjust to a new and greatly reduced scale when evaluating plant growth. The 3-inch growth of a first year live oak seedling is a wonderous thing. If it tops 5 inches by the end of the second year, growth is very satisfactory (Fig. 27).

It has been noticed that many newly planted woody plants have a tough time of it for the first three or four years.

Fig. 26 Woody planting tests. Hammocks Beach State Park, North Carolina.

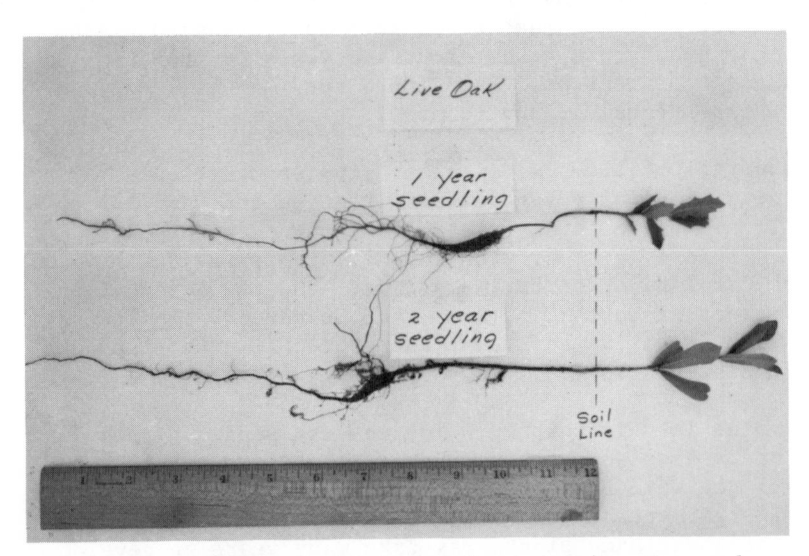

Fig. 27 Live oak (*Quercus virginiana*). One and two year old seedlings which grew on dune sand.

Then suddenly they seem to take new life. This may be explained by the theory that such plants are developing deep root systems during the first few years. When the root finally taps a deep and adequate source of water, the above ground parts of the plant respond. A live oak seedling which is 3/4 tap root, seems to bear out this idea.

SPECIES

After five years of evaluating woody perennials for dune plantings, the following are among the best for this work. These are plants which, after receiving the needed cultural practices for establishment, can be expected to maintain themselves on the dunes with a minimum amount of care. Many more plants remain to be tested. Additional promising plants are found in the table in Section 5.

TREES - Eastern redcedar - *Juniperus virginiana*
Live oak - *Quercus virginiana*

SHRUBS - Northern bayberry - *Myrica pensylvanica*
Eastern baccharis - *Baccharis halimifolia*
Yaupon holly - *Ilex vomitoria*
*Thorny elaeagnus - *Elaeagnus pungens*
*False anil indigo - *Indigofera pseudotinctoria*
*Salt cedar - *Tamarix gallica*
Marsh elder - *Iva imbricata*
Yucca - *Yucca* sp.

VINES - Virginia creeper - *Parthenocissus quinquifolia*
Muscadine grape - *Vitus rotundifolia*
Wild bamboo - *Smilax auriculata*

*Introduced species (all others are native).

One of the most promising species for dune stabilization and beautification is northern bayberry (Fig. 28). Its good adaptation and colonizing habit of growth makes it a prime "suspect" in our search for the "best one."

TIME OF PLANTING

Woody stock can be put in any time during the dormant season. The optimum time is February. This puts the plant out there and ready to grow just before the growing season. It reduces the time the plant is subjected to cold, drying winter winds.

Fig. 28 A two year transplant of northern bayberry showing spread from new sprouts. Emerald Isle, North Carolina.

FERTILIZERS AND ORGANIC AMENDMENTS

Great care must be taken in the use of fertilizer at planting time. This warning is especially significant at the beach. Fertilizer should not be mixed with the sand which goes back around the roots of the plants. Drying of this sand during droughty summer periods tends to concentrate the dissolved fertilizer salts. This can severely injure plant root systems.

The use of fertilizer in our first year tests resulted in poor seedling survival. Check plots without fertilizer almost always faired best. Sharp (15) also concluded in his New Jersey work on the dunes that there was no advantage in applying fertilizer at planting time. In spite of these findings, it was felt that the problem lay with the type and amounts of fertilizers used and the methods of application. During the following two years, planting trials were established to explore these possibilities. Several treatments showed an immediate first year increase in the survival and growth of transplants.

Good results were had with "fortified organics." Dried peat moss, rotted sawdust, or 1/2 inch ground pine bark is used as a base. A "starter" solution (water plus liquid fertilizer) is made according to the directions on the bottle of fertilizer. The strength is that as recommended for fertilizing shrubbery. Any liquid fertilizer with a generous supply of nitrogen will work. A substitute solution may be made by adding a heaping tablespoon of 8-8-8 or 10-10-10 fertilizer to a gallon of water. It is ready to use after stirring and allowing it to set over night. The liquid is then used to wet the dried organic material. A pint of this mix is dropped in each planting hole. It is mixed about half and half with sand before setting the plant. Seedlings thrive on this mixture. After a season's growth, plant roots form a dense, tangled mass in the enriched humus. Seaside gardeners have a high regard for peat moss as an additive in dune plantings. Results of our state park tests showed that it was only slightly better than rotted sawdust or finely ground pine bark.

Any of these organic materials improve the sand (Fig. 29). They help to retain moisture and plant food and are a

Fig. 29 A seedling being planted in a hole in which peat moss (as shown on left) has been mixed with the sand.

source of beneficial bacteria. When starter solutions are added, their value is increased. The organic substance tends to "safen" the fertilizer as well as retain it. Pine bark absorbs the liquid slowly but will finally become completely saturated. As the bark gradually breaks down in the soil, it acts as a slow release mechanism for the plant nutrients.

Another successful fertilizing device is the plastic envelope of fertilizer. This is a commercial product called "Rootcontact Paket." These are 3 1/2 by 3 1/2 inches in size and hold one ounce of highly soluble 16-8-16 fertilizer. The packs are sealed but pierced four times through both sides with a needle. These are placed in the planting holes near the plant roots. Due to hydroscopic action, moisture accumulates in the pack until it finally begins to leak out. This slow leakage is capable of feeding the plant for two or more years. In our test, one "Paket" plus one-half gallon of wet peat moss was used around each plant. Plants so treated showed a marked increase in first year quality and vigor of growth (Fig. 30).

Fig. 30 Virginia creeper transplant after three months of growth. Plant in foreground with Rootcontact Paket; plant to rear, no treatment.

In a third treatment, "Agriform Planting Tablets" were used. This is a compressed "pill" weighing 21 grams. It is composed of a very slowly dissolvable 20-10-5 fertilizer. Since bacterial action is needed to help break down this fertilizer, wet peat moss was mixed into each planting hole. This treatment was also beneficial with no adverse effect on transplanted seedlings.

Lastly, as a check to represent a more standard procedure, the common 8-8-8 fertilizer was used in two ways: first, an ounce was scattered in a 1-foot circle around each freshly planted plant; and second, after planting, two slits (6 inches from the stem) were made in the sand with a trowel. A half ounce of 8-8-8 was dropped in each slit and then covered. Both of these treatments improved plant growth the first year.

The following observations can be made: None of the treatments above showed any evidence of root burn. The survival of plants was excellent. The first year nourishment may have actually carried some of the weaker plants through the season. There was also a definite increase of growth and plant quality. The fortified organics produced the quickest and most luxuriant growth. The plastic packs with wet peat most were next in effectiveness with planting tablets plus peat moss close behind. The 8-8-8 applications were satisfactory. They were not quite as effective as those above but they were significantly better than the check plots.

The figures of our 1972 tests have just been tabulated. The results are interesting even though some of them will bear rechecking next year. For example, fortified organic material (1 pint) added to Agriform Plant Tablets or Rootcontact Pakets increased their effectiveness. And "Osmocote," a slow release 18-6-12 fertilizer which is pelleted inside a plastic coating, was equally as good. After planting, a half ounce of this material was placed in each of two trowel slits 6 inches from the plant stems.

To summarize this fertilizer information: Our average cottager will not recognize all of this as one giant step ahead for anybody. He and others, with little time and with no consuming interest in plants, may simply broadcast an ounce of 8-8-8 or 10-10-10 on the surface after plants begin to grow. Larger amounts should be used for balled and burlapped stock. Fertilizer wedged into the bottom of the holes at planting time will also be beneficial. Other folks with the needed time and interest can experiment with fortified organics and try some of the products listed. For those who have a professional interest in the problem, this information could provide some logical starting points for further investigations.

TOPSOIL AS AN AMENDMENT

A safe and easy method for starting off transplant stock in the dunes is to replace the sand in the planting hole with topsoil. A shovel full of fertile soil will supply the necessities for successful plant establishment (Fig. 31). Two shovels of soil are better, three are better than two - and so on. A pile of good topsoil to be used

Fig. 31 Two year old Japanese black pine on Sullivans Island, South Carolina, responded to a shovel of topsoil under each plant. E. T. Simons, Jr., Soil Conservation Technician.

as needed is really an essential for anyone who will be transplanting perennials. Lugging the heavy soil around is a disadvantage. This is not a serious drawback for the cottager working with only a small number of plants. For large-scale dune plantings involving hundreds or perhaps thousands of plants, this method is likely to be impractical. Yet, it remains a gardener's favorite. Once the soil is put under the plant, its beneficial properties become a long lasting boon to plant growth. And, of course, with such plantings the fortified organics, fertilizer pack, or tablet may be added. If not, the regular 8-8-8 fertilizer may be broadcast on the surface later after growth starts.

PLANTING

Dry, windy days on the beach are common. The roots of planting stock must be protected from drying out. A plastic sack used to carry the plants will keep them moist. On bright days a burlap or paper sack used as an outside cover will keep out the sunlight and reduce the heat inside the sack.

After setting the plant, the sand must be packed tightly around the roots with the heel. The optimum method is to water the sand or soil as it is replaced. This runs the sand together and brings it into the closest possible contact with the roots.

Dry sand which runs down into the planting hole can be troublesome. Sand in that condition is often very difficult to wet. A good practice is to scrape much of this surface sand to one side before starting the hole.

The depth at which the plant is set should be about 2 inches deeper than it grew in the nursery. Then, as a finishing touch, some of this extra depth of sand around the plant may be removed leaving a bowl-shaped depression. This facilitates later watering; and too, beach plants are better off if they are set a little deeper than they grew in the nursery.

MULCHING

Dead American beachgrass placed around newly set thorny elaeagnus plants improved the quality and vigor of growth. Enough grass was used to completely hide the sand in a 16 inch circle around each plant. Sand drifted into this mulch and partly buried it.

Other tests included half-gallon amounts of pine or hardwood bark used as a mulch around each plant. This failed to produce any noticeable benefit. One can speculate as to the reasons behind these divergent results. But further work in this field will be necessary to find the correct answer.

In landscape work where topsoil has been used, the use of mulch is a standard and proven practice.

DIRECT SEEDING

The planting of live oak (*Quercus virginiana*) acorns in sand dune areas has been successful. The acorns are collected in October as soon as they fall from the trees. They may be planted immediately or later during the winter months. If it is necessary to keep them for more than two weeks after collection, they should be put in plastic bags, mixed with damp sand and refrigerated at 36° to 40°. The mix by volume is about 3/5 sand to 2/5 acorns. The bags must be checked occasionally to see that the sand does not dry out. Stored in this manner seed can be kept in good shape through March to early April. Sprouting in cold storage will begin in early spring. The seed must then be planted with little further delay.

The optimum planting time is in the fall. The acorns will quickly sprout and start putting down a tap root before cold weather. The nuts are planted 1 1/2 up to 2 inches deep. No fertilizer should be used at planting time.

Mice will often find and eat the acorns during the winter months. Damage can be particularly severe when plantings are made in dune areas with good grass cover. Such plantings can be saved by treating the acorns with a chemical rodent deterrent.

Fall and winter planted nuts will start coming up in late April. Emergence is irregular - sometimes requiring five or six weeks. In my plantings, I averaged about 70 seedlings for each 100 acorns planted.

Growth is slow (Fig. 32). At this stage, most of the growth is taking place beneath the surface. Seedlings should be fertilized lightly at mid-season of the first summer and then each spring. Our four year old plants treated this way are now (only) a foot tall.

Another plant which was successful from a direct sand dune seeding is wild bamboo (*Smilax auriculata*) (Fig. 33). The catch - seedlings came up two and a half years after the seeds were planted. Yet, this does not pose a difficult problem. For nursery production, seed could be collected and stored in refrigerators each year. After two years, this would provide a continuous series of seed lots ready to germinate. In the field, seed could simply be collected and planted each year. After the waiting period, each lot would come at its appointed time.

Fig. 32 Live oak seedlings about four months old.

Fig. 33 Wild bamboo (*Smilax auriculata*) seed planted in dune sand December 1969, sprouted in April 1972.

Marsh elder (*Iva imbricata*) seed collected in the fall, stored dry, and spring planted did not germinate. This same lot of seed mixed with damp peat moss and refrigerated for three weeks before planting also did not germinate.

Yet this plant has definite direct seeding possibilities. In nature, seedlings are commonly found where the sand is damp - even on the beach just above the high tide mark. Fall planting may be the answer. In the early spring young native seedlings transplant easily but grew slowly (Fig. 34).

Fig. 34 Marsh elder (*Iva imbricata*) first year seedlings.

Wax myrtle (*Myrica cerifera*) and northern bayberry (*Myrica pensylvanica*) both fall planted on dune sand failed to germinate. Both of these come easily from seed if handled this way on the heavier inland soil types. With little doubt, the droughtiness of the top several inches of dune sand is responsible for this difficulty.

MAINTENANCE

The term "establishment" as applied to plants has been defined in several ways. For woody dune plantings, it is the time required for a young plant to develop enough leaf surface and root system to maintain itself in a growing, healthy condition without further help from man.

This time period for plants at the beach is longer than average. The various plant species will differ in their needs. A three or four year establishment period with fertilizer applied each spring should take care of most species. A rounded tablespoon of a "complete" fertilizer (8-8-8, 10-10-10, etc.) broadcast in a 1-foot circle around each plant is the easiest method. This may be improved by placing the fertilizer in two slits 6 inches from the stem. Most seaside gardeners with relatively few woody transplants will want to hurry the plants by fertilizing them every year.

Our past tests show that even well adapted native dune transplants are subject to high mortality rates and have great difficulty in becoming established without improving the fertility of the sand.

SECTION 4

BEACH LANDSCAPING

This section deals with the art of landscaping around and in the yard areas of cottages or other buildings at the beach. The principles of landscaping at the beach are the same as anywhere else. It is suggested that the reader secure copies of "Landscaping Your Home," Extension Circular No. 476, North Carolina Agricultural Extension Service, North Carolina State University, Raleigh, North Carolina; or "Landscape Planning for South Carolina Homes," Circular 526, Agricultural Extension Service, Clemson University, Clemson, South Carolina. While these general rules apply, beach work requires changes in planting procedures and the use of plants which are adapted to seaside conditions.

SELECTION OF PLANTS

When it comes to landscape or dune control plantings there are some purist who would select and use only native plants. This is an admirable approach. I would be a bit more lenient. There are many introduced plants which are adapted to the seashore. To use them is to take advantage of an additional large array of desirable and interesting plant characteristics. For some purposes, these plants will out-do the natives.

The table in Section 5 and the individual plant descriptions which follow has been prepared to assist the reader in making plant selections.

PRE-PLANNING AND PREPARING THE SITE

Many years are involved in the vegetative development of a mature dune landscape. But man, in his thoughtless and unrestrained way, takes only a few hours to bulldoze and destroy what has taken nature ages to perfect. In too many instances, the word "development" has become synonymous with the greatest calamity which can befall a beach area. The "developers" are usually saddled with all the blame for mishandling the land. This is rarely true. We must remember that individuals who buy the property do a tremendous amount of damage. Many a beautiful beach site is sold and then stripped of vegetation and flattened by the bulldozers as a matter of course. This has been called a relic reaction still surviving from the pioneer days when man was pitted against nature for living space.

There are many good examples where the works of man have been established in harmony with the land. They are the result of careful planning based on a knowledge of the natural processes, the capabilities of the soil coupled with the principles of good land use and a general appreciation of natural beauty.

District conservationists of the Soil Conservation Service are recognized professionals in this work. Landowners are encouraged to call on them for technical assistance in planning beach projects.

It is a lucky landowner who starts with a lot which has some grass, shrub, or tree cover. Grading for the building site should be planned to disturb this native growth as little as possible (Fig. 35). Very special consideration should be given to valuable specimens of native shrubs, trees, and vines. Usually, skillful planning can utilize the natural contours of the land to good effect in the landscape plan. After the building site, driveway, and parking area have been graded there may be little need for any additional leveling. We're at the beach - remember? Why not preserve its natural appearance as much as possible?

But let's face it - many people will not have these choices. They will start with the purchase of a lot which has already been bulldozed "flat as a pancake." So the only alternative is to set to work with plants to enhance the beauty of that barren plot of sand and restrain it from moving elsewhere during the next high wind.

Fig. 35 A beach home set unobtrusively into the existing natural cover of yaupon holly, live oak, etc. Emerald Isle, North Carolina.

The planting sites for each species must be planned so that the salt-hardy ones will occupy the most exposed positions. Less tolerant plants must be further away from the sea or furnished protection.

The lee side of a cottage offers good protection; but just beyond it, plants are often in the "slip-stream" of salt wind concentrated along the side of the building (Fig. 36).

At this juncture, with the general planting layout in mind, the gardener's best friend is topsoil. Good sandy loam (if possible) spread generously over all areas where lawn or shrubs, etc., are to be planted is a necessity. The driveway might be coated too. It will provide a good driving surface at least temporarily. Later, it will make a good base for asphalt or gravel.

The recommended amount of soil to use varies greatly, simply because it is a "more the better" kind of situation. Menninger (13) in his book "Seaside Plants of the World" advises a foot of topsoil for seaside gardens. The views of local nurserymen seem to average out something like this:

(1) For lawns - 3 to 4 inches minimum depth and up to 8 inches for very satisfactory results;

(2) For gardens, foundation planting, etc. - 8 inches minimum on up to 1 foot for very satisfactory results.

Fig. 36 California privet (*Ligustrum ovalifolium*) takes a beating from salt winds where it extends beyond the protection of a cottage. Emerald Isle, North Carolina.

The topsoil should be mixed with several inches of the underlying sand. This can be done when fertilizer and lime (if needed) is mixed into the soil. It is a good idea to have an extra pile of soil dumped off to one side and left unspread. This will be used later when the shrubs and other woody species are planted.

The soil which has been hauled in may have a very acid reaction not conducive to good plant growth. Mixing this soil with some of the underlying beach sand may completely correct this condition since the sand with many fine shell fragments usually has a pH range from 6.5 (very slightly acid) to neutral 7.0 or even alkaline to about 8.0. A sample may be sent off to the state soil testing laboratory to determine the lime and fertilizer needs. Without such a test, 50 pounds of agricultural limestone and about 15 pounds of 5-10-10 or 6-12-12 fertilizer (or approximate equivalent) should be broadcast for each 1,000 square feet. These should be worked into the soil. A rototiller type machine is excellent for this purpose.

PLANTING

Let's first be sure that we eliminate the most common error. It has to do with the spacing of plants in foundation plantings. Most everyone, except the nurserymen, crowd their plants too close to the sides of the building, and, for that matter, too close to the edges of drives, walkways, etc. The large shrubs such as *Pittosporum, Ligustrum, Euonymus, Ilex* (yaupon), *Elaeagnus, Raphiolepsis, Myrica, Nerium,* and others are often used around buildings. Their growth in width is in the six to eight foot range. If planted 4 feet from the cottage, moderate pruning will keep them in bounds. For smaller shrubs - the low junipers, hollies, yucca, etc. - the clearance should be reduced to 3 feet. Adequate space between the foundation planting and the cottage will help to keep branches from scrubbing against the building. It will also provide welcome access for the incessant maintenance jobs such as painting.

Bare rooted planting stock should be kept moist at all times. Plants which have been grown in pots or cans may be root bound. If the roots are matted around the outside of the root ball, slash them 1/2 inch deep down the sides and across the bottom. Three or four cuts evenly spaced will short circuit the long winding trip for plant food and stimulate lateral root growth.

Holes which are dug for transplanting balled and burlapped stock should be at least twice as big around in all directions as needed to accommodate the roots. When smaller stock is used (such as in gallon cans) the holes should also be generously large - something like 18 inches across. The roots will soon require a great deal of additional space if they are to support a healthy plant.

Sites for the planting holes must be improved by replacing two to four buckets of the sand with topsoil. The amount depends somewhat on the size and kind of plant - but mainly on the interest and stamina of the plantsman. In topsoiled areas of the yard, less sand will need to be removed. In deeply topsoiled areas for foundation plantings or gardens, it may not be necessary to take out any sand.

So, with the hole opened, the topsoil is dumped in, a bucket-full at a time, and mixed with the sand along the sides and bottom of the hole. A mix of two-thirds soil with one-third sand to a depth of 16 to 24 inches is a general guide.

After the soil has been prepared, the hole is opened to the correct planting depth. Two or three slits are then wedged open in the bottom of the hole with the spade. They should be about 4 inches deep. In each, a half ounce (one rounded tablespoon) of fertilizer is dropped. The slits are then closed over and the hole is ready for planting. Never mix fertilizer with the soil which goes back around the roots. However, an "Agriform Planting Tablet" or a "Rootcontact Paket" may be used without danger (see fertilizers under "Woody Plantings for Dune Protection" in Section 3). The soil is then tamped down around the roots of the plant. When the hole is about half filled the plant should be watered. After the water drains away the filling and packing is completed. A low dam in the form of a ring of soil is left around the base of the plant to hold water. The plant is then ready for a final watering. The coarse grade of ground pine bark placed around the base of the shrubs and trees will reduce weed growth and evaporation and give the job a finishing touch.

If no fertilizer was used in the hole at planting time, it may be broadcast on the surface after plant growth starts. An ounce of 8-8-8 or 10-10-10 for the average gallon container plant will stimulate growth.

A growing number of seaside gardeners recommend the use of peat moss. A bucket of this moistened material mixed into the soil around and below the roots of the plant is beneficial. Peat moss aids in absorbing and holding moisture and plant nutrients. This is especially important during dry times if the cottager cannot tend to his plants frequently.

SALT WIND BARRIERS

Salt wind barriers serve several purposes and deserve special mention (Fig. 37). They may be used to shield gardens of plants subject to salt burn. They help protect buildings from storm winds, deflect wind driven salt and sand from parked cars, keep out trespassers, and screen off unsightly areas. A wide, well developed vegetative barrier will also moderate traffic racket.

An "instant" screen or wind barrier can be had by installing a fence (Fig. 38). A solid wall is not as effective as a fence with a slatted board arrangement where

Fig. 37 A rugged salt wind shrub barrier. Sullivans Island, South Carolina.

Fig. 38 An "instant" saltwind barrier of slatted redwood. Wright Brothers National Memorial, Kill Devil Hills, North Carolina. Yaupon holly in the foreground.

approximately 40 percent of the surface is void and 60 percent is wood or other material. Ordinary snow fence, though only 4 feet tall, comes close to these specifications with a 50:50 ratio. This type of construction will reduce wind velocities up to 80 percent. It will afford protection on the lee side as far as two to four times the height of the fence. Its effects will be felt as far as ten times the height. Vegetative barriers will have these same modifying effects.

Many patterns for barriers constructed of wood are available. Cement blocks set on edge to reveal an open or "see through" design are substantial and maintenance free. But for the plantsman, a vegetative barrier is much more intriguing. Several conditions and natural forces must be considered:

At the beach, the seaward side of natural shrub growth is wind-trimmed down to a thin "cutting edge." The lower branches are protected by beach grasses or other herbaceous vegetation. The shrubs behind this first line of defense get progressively taller as each plant helps to shield the one behind. In cross section, the barrier becomes wedge shaped - low in front and taller to the rear. In badly exposed sand dune areas it is especially important to remember this principle. Extremely salt-hardy plants indigenous to the pioneer zone may be planted as a low growing first row. Plants such as seaoats (*Uniola paniculata*), marsh elder (*Iva imbricata*), *Panicum amarulum*, adamsneedle (*Yucca filamentosa*), and hairawn muhly (*Muhlenbergia capillaris*) are good choices for such lead rows. Taller plants starting with the most salt tolerant ones would follow in rows behind.

The second condition to be reckoned with is the soil site. Usually there are two - either pure dune sand, or sand which has been improved with topsoil. If on dune sand, plants for the more rearward rows should be selected from the table in Section 5 which are marked for dune erosion control as well as for salt wind barriers. On improved soils any plants marked for salt wind barriers may be used. Select double x-ed (XX) plants if such stock is available.

When possible, evergreen plants should be favored since they give maximum year around protection. However, two of the better barrier shrubs, eastern baccharis and salt cedar, should not be overlooked. A close planting of either one will provide a very satisfactory tangle of stems.

The rows which make up the bulk of the barrier may be one or several species. If several species are used, their ultimate height as well as their salt tolerance should determine their position in the barrier.

Up to a certain point, the height of protection increases with each added row. Two rows of evergreen shrubs is close to a minimum, and three to six rows should take care of most other conditions.

Plant spacings for the large growing *Pittosporum, Euonymus, Ligustrum, Zanthoxylum,* and *Elaeagnus* are 3 feet in the row with 5-foot middles; for *Baccharis, Tamarix,* and *Myrica*, 2 feet by 3 feet. *Yucca* plants should be 2 feet apart in a first row position. Grasses are best with a 1 to 1 1/2 foot spacing.

LAWNS

Surprisingly, the beach gardener has a good selection of grasses from which he may choose. The grasses as a group seem to be more tolerant to salt spray than most broad-leaved plants. Then too, it is possible that at ground level they are less exposed to salt accumulations. In observing the lawns along the coast, it was found that three species predominate: centipedegrass (*Eremochloa ophiuroides*); bermudagrass (*Cynodon dactylon*); and St. Augustine - or Charlestongrass - (*Stenotaphrum secundatum*). For beach lawns, the first two species lead by a wide margin. Two other grasses, bahiagrass (*Paspalum notatum*) and zoyzia (*Zoyzia matrella*), are gaining favor at the beaches but are still quite scarce. No lawns of tall fescue (*Festuca arundinacea)* were found - at least not in close proximity to the ocean. There may be some. Stray clumps were noticed occasionally in places exposed to the ocean. Most of these were uncut and the long leaves had taken some tip burn. With proper mowing (2 1/2 to 3 inches) it seems likely that this species might be acceptable under certain conditions. Tolerance of fescue to salt has been recognized by Menninger (13). Its most serious enemy would be summer heat and drought. Certainly it would have no chance at all without a very generous layer of topsoil. It would also die if buried by sand. The northern part of the Carolina coast would be more favorable for its growth.

The species described below are recommended. They are "warm season" perennials - green and growing in the summer, dead and brown in the winter. This growth habit corresponds exactly with the beach "season" - a very convenient arrangement.

CENTIPEDEGRASS is very popular and is my first choice (Fig. 39). At Myrtle Beach and south, the popularity of

Fig. 39 A centipede lawn close to the ocean at Myrtle Beach, South Carolina. A low but growing shrub barrier helps to ward off salt winds.

this species is challenged by St. Augustine. Centipede will take more abuse, grow on the poorest sites and will get along with less attention than any other lawn grass. A small 6-inch square planted on pure dune sand has survived from year to year and sent out long runners with only one moderate fertilization each spring. It will grow in full sun to partial shade, and has only above ground runners. This makes it easier to control than bermudagrass.

Centipede is best established by planting the runners. Seed is available but such plantings often fail for lack of water during the owners absence. Runners are planted (leaving some tip leaves exposed) on one or two foot centers, depending upon the cottager's patience. Growth is quite slow, but inexorable. Two to three years are needed to attain full cover. Thereafter, it should receive only one moderate fertilization in the spring and mowed about every three weeks.

Centipede thrives on soils which are somewhat acid. Lime should not be used if the pH is 5.8 or greater. If the soil becomes alkaline in reaction, centipedegrass may turn yellow. This is due to a lack of iron. It can be corrected temporarily by spraying the turf with a solution containing 1 tablespoon of iron sulphate in 2 gallons of water per 50 square feet (11).

A high level of phosphorous in the soil is also harmful. Fertilizers which are high in nitrogen and low in phosphorous should be used.

BERMUDAGRASS comes in many forms, from the fine almost moss-like types used on golf greens to the much coarser "common" and the exuberant hay and pasture type called 'Coastal.' The main objection to the fine bladed 'Tift' types is that their velvety beauty is considerably marred by any other grass or weed which may come up in them. Because of this and the extra maintenance suggested, they may not be practical for the beach addict who would rather spend his time fishing than digging lawn weeds. If a hybrid is desired, one of the best is 'Tifway' (T419) which is moderately fine bladed, disease resistant, dark green, and entirely desirable for an intensively used high-quality lawn (Fig. 40). A well versed nurseryman at Pawley's Island, South Carolina, uses this selection for most of his beach lawn jobs (and prefers to use 3 inches of topsoil on top of 4 inches of clay as a base).

Fig. 40 'Tifway' (T419) bermudagrass used for a putting green on a golf course. "Seascape" Development, Kitty Hawk, North Carolina. J. D. Ruffner, Northeast Plant Materials Specialist, and W. W. Steiner, Head Plant Materials Specialist, USDA - SCS.

Another excellent choice is 'Tufcote' bermudagrass, a recent introduction by the Soil Conservation Service. It is another hybrid which is an extremely wiry, vigorous, traffic resistant selection. It is midway in coarseness between the fine bermudas and common and would not show weed encroachment as badly.

A third hybrid, useful at the beach but not a lawn type, is Coastal bermudagrass, the "jolly green giant" of pastures. This one will perform better than all other bermudas on the poorest sand soils and is also very salt tolerant. Fertilized once a year, it will thrive on sites which are only one grade better than dune sand. This would include dredged sand and hydraulic fills. A good planting of this is found at the ferry landing at Fort Fisher, North Carolina. It is also effective on low maintenance areas where only a small amount of topsoil has been added (Fig. 41). The long runners and tall growth produces a very open sod which should be mowed only occasionally to a 4 inch height. Since none of these hybrid bermudas produce seed, sprigs must be used for establishing plantings.

Fig. 41 Lawn of 'Coastal' bermudagrass used in a low traffic area where a minimum of topsoil was used. The shrubs are eastern baccharis. Emerald Isle, North Carolina.

Still another choice and one which may be the most practical is "common" bermudagrass. It is used for the majority of bermudagrass lawns at the beach. Both seed and sprigs of this one are readily available and cheap.

Bermudagrass has a well known reputation for salt resistance. Common bermudagrass has recovered even after flooding with sea water. Growth is very fast and a full cover may be expected in the first year. Runners above ground and rhizomes below make it difficult to control. In short order it can become an aggravating pest in shrubbery and adjoining gardens. To keep any lawn type bermudagrass at its best, it should be fertilized liberally and mowed once a week.

The grass has a super ability to resist sand burial, a very important consideration for lawns close to bare areas of moving sand. Winter drifts of sand up to 2 feet deep on Atlantic Beach lawns are cleared each spring with no detriment to the following summer growth of the grass (Fig. 42).

Tufcote, Coastal, and all of the fine bermudas are hybrids. They produce almost no seed and must be sprigged. Common

Fig. 42 Back-to-back lawns of "common" bermudagrass face the ocean at Atlantic Beach, North Carolina.

bermudagrass may be sprigged or seeded. Plant spacing is about 2 feet, except for Coastal which can be opened up to 3 feet. All of them require a sunny location.

All bermudagrasses except Coastal are mowed about 1 inch high. Coastal should be cut 2 to 4 inches tall.

ST. AUGUSTINE is a lush, wide-bladed species with above ground runners. In South Carolina, it is often called Charlestongrass. It is dependably hardy northward only to about Atlantic Beach, North Carolina (Fig. 43). It has a good salt tolerance and has the very important ability of growing well in the shade. The vigorous growth makes a dense mat which discourages weed invasion. The species has a serious drawback in its susceptibility to damage by chinch bugs. Often these pests create large brown spots before the damage is recognized. In addition, this grass is not as drought hardy nor will it grow on as poor a site as centipede or bermudagrass. It will respond well to good moisture and high fertility. St. Augustine should be mowed 1 1/2 to 2 1/2 inches high. Sprigs must be used in planting.

ZOYZIAGRASS or MANILLAGRASS has fine dark green leaves and spreads slowly from above ground runners and to a lesser degree from rhizomes under the surface. It is only moderately tolerant to drought but has good salt spray

Fig. 43 A well kept St. Augustine lawn at Morehead City, North Carolina. It is sprayed regularly for chinch bug control.

resistance. Contrary to popular opinion, it must be mowed frequently - about once every seven to ten days and to a height of 1 to 1 1/2 inches. Zoyzia lawns are dense and develop a thatch of dead clippings which must be removed once a year by a close clipping and raking in the early spring.

Other zoyzias are 'Emerald' - a cross between *Z. japonica* and *Z. tenuifolia* - and 'Meyer,' which is a selection out of *Z. japonica*. Manillagrass (*Z. matrella*) is said to be superior to these for seaside plantings because of its higher tolerance to salt winds (12).

The grass is established by sprigging or plugging on one foot centers (Fig. 44). Growth is slow and it takes about three years for a full cover to develop.

BAHIAGRASS (Fig. 45) is a native species of South America. The two most important selections are 'Pensacola' and 'Wilmington.' Both were found at those respective seacoast ports in the South and developed by the Soil Conservation Service. Wilmington is darker green, more cold-hardy, and makes a tighter sod than Pensacola. The seeds of Wilmington are about a quarter larger than those of Pensacola.

Fig. 44 Cutting up strips of *Zoyia matrella* sod for planting a beach lawn. Emerald Isle, North Carolina.

Bahiagrass will do well on relatively poor sites, and has excellent salt spray tolerance. The seeds are borne in a "V" shaped head. These start appearing in late June and keep reappearing consistently soon after each mowing

Fig. 45 An uncut lawn of'Pensacola' bahiagrass showing "V" shaped seed heads. Litchfield Beach, South Carolina.

until late in the summer. Most people regard this as objectionable. The grass is disease free, traffic resistant, and requires little maintenance except for mowing. Mowing height is 1 to 1 1/2 inches. Both are established from seed.

Pensacola seed is readily available in South Carolina. Seed of Wilmington is scarce. Sources may be furnished by the Soil Conservation Service upon inquiry.

PLANTING NURSERY STOCK IN ESTABLISHED LAWNS

Special precautions are needed when trees and shrubs are to be set in a bermudagrass lawn. This grass is a fierce competitor. Before transplanting, all the underground grass roots must be removed within a 1 1/2 to 2 foot circle. A metal collar (usually 10-inch wide aluminum) is placed around the perimeter of the hole (Fig. 46). The

Fig. 46 Getting ready to plant a Brazilian butia seedling in a bermudagrass lawn. The aluminum collar will keep grass roots from competing.

stock is then planted. About 1/2 inch of the metal is left above the surface. A depression left around the plant facilitates watering (Fig. 47).

Fig. 47 A depression left around the plant retains the water applied after planting.

Subsurface metal collars around transplants are not nearly as necessary in centipede, St. Augustine, or bahiagrass lawns. These grasses have above ground runners (stolons) rather than underground rhizomes. However, metal rings protruding above the surface will facilitate the control of grass runners.

Zoyziagrass has both above and below ground runners, but it spreads slowly. Metal guards (as used in bermudagrass sod) are very helpful but not absolutely necessary.

After the nursery stock gains in size and leafiness, the competing grass is largely shaded out. There are exceptions to this. A notable example is the ragged looking sight of bermudagrass growing through the low or shrub type junipers.

SECTION 5

EVALUATION OF PERENNIAL BEACH PLANTS

EXPLANATION OF EVALUATION TABLE

The plants which appear in the following table are those which occur most frequently on Carolina beach areas. In a few cases, species much less prominent were included when the specimens found showed good adaptability. The selection of all plants was based on their current usefulness as landscape subjects or their use or apparent adaptability as sand stilling plants in the dune areas. No effort was made to expand the list with "possibilities." There are many such plants both native and exotic which remain to be studied and evaluated for beach work in the Carolinas. The authority used for all plant names is the 1942 second edition of "Standardized Plant Names" by McFarland.

In the first column, the plants are listed alphabetically by scientific name. The common name follows. Local common names are occasionally included. They are grouped in four categories: shrubs, trees, vines, and herbaceous plants. Plants which are native to the Carolinas are followed by an asterisk.

The second and third columns, "Resistance to Salt Wind Burn" and "Vigor of Growth" are evaluated by numbers from one (excellent) down to four, which is mediocre. To further explain how this applies to salt wind resistance: Plants with a No. 1 rating are those which require no protection from ocean winds. All others need some degree of protection. The No. 4 group requires the most. Protection is afforded by placing some kind of barrier between the plant in question and the damaging ocean winds, by increasing the distance between the plant and the sea, or by a combination of both.

The less intensive salt spray factor along South Carolina beaches was in some cases too mild to really test the inherent resistance of several species. Therefore, the ratings are based mainly on observations taken on the more rigorous North Carolina beaches.

These evaluations were confirmed in South Carolina, where the differences in tolerance between species was almost always apparent but on a more moderated scale. This gives the South Carolina gardener an edge on his northern counterpart. For example, Japanese privet and yaupon holly (both No. 3 in the table) require the protection of buildings, etc., at Emerald Isle, North Carolina. But these same plants are found only nipped and wind trimmed (as No. 2) around exposed cottage fronts at Myrtle Beach, South Carolina. Therefore, ratings are based on my judgment after observing these plants on many occasions "from Nags Head to Hilton Head." There is nothing absolute about these values. They are meant to give the reader some comparative data which will help him make good use of plants at the beach.

Concerning the fourth column - "Average Height in Feet": The first figure indicates the average height one may expect at the beach and in areas moderately close to the ocean. The second figure is the potential height of the plant in a better environment - sometimes found in the "back areas" of the beach.

For the next six columns in the table, X's are used to affirm the plant's qualification under various headings. A double X means that the plant is particularly well qualified for the indicated use. "Landscaping" in Column eight refers to plantings around buildings and the immediate yard areas where the site will be improved considerably with topsoil and other additives. "Dune Erosion Control" in Column nine refers to plantings in dune areas (usually in stands of grass and herbaceous vegetation) where the site will not usually be improved with additions of topsoil.

The final column gives the page number where a description of the plant and notes on its use may be found.

EVALUATION TABLE

PERENNIAL SEASIDE PLANTS FOR THE CAROLINAS

SPECIES	Resists Salt Windburn	Vigor of Growth	Average Height in feet	Ever-green	Good For:				General Use		See Page
					Clipped Hedges	Salt Wind Barrier	Screens	Bird Food	Land scaping	Dune Erosion Control	
SHRUBS											
Baccharis halimifolia L. * Eastern Baccharis	1[a]	2[a]	5-12			XX	X			XX	81
Callicarpa americana L. * American Beautyberry	3	3	3-5					X	X	X	83
Cleyera japonica Sieb. & Zucc. Cleyera	3	3	6-8	X	X		X		X		85
Daubentonia punicea Cav. * Rattlebox	3	3	5-7						X	X	86
Elaeagnus pungens Thunbg. Thorny Elaeagnus	1	1	6-10	X	X	XX	XX	X	XX	X	88
Euonymus japonicus L. Evergreen Euonymus	1	2	7-13	X	X	XX	XX		XX		90
Fatshedera x lizei Tree Ivy	4	2	5-7	X					X		93
Fatsia japonica Decne & Planch. Japanese Fatsia	4	3	5-15	X					X		94
Hydrangea macrophylla D. C. Bigleaf Hydrangea	3	2	3-8						X		96

* Native Plants

(a)Resistance to salt burn and vigor of growth rated by numbers: 1 = excellent (to) 4 = mediocre.
X Indicates plants best use; XX is used to denote choice selections.

SPECIES	Resists Salt Windburn	Vigor of Growth	Average Height in feet	Ever-green	Good For:				General Use		See Page
					Clipped Hedges	Salt Wind Barrier	Screens	Bird Food	Land-scaping	Dune Erosion Control	
Ilex vomitoria Ait. * Yaupon Holly	3	4	10-24	X	X		X	X	XX	X	97
Indigofera pseudotinctoria Matsum. False Anil Indigo	2	3	1-2						X	X	99
Iva imbricata Walter. * Marsh Elder	1	2	1-3			X				XX	101
Juniperus chinensis var. pfitzeriana Spaeth. Pfitzer Juniper	4	4	3-4	X					X		104
Juniperus conferta Parl. Shore Juniper	3	3	1	X					XX		105
Ligustrum japonicum Thunb. Japanese Privet	3	2	4-16	X			X	X	X		107
Ligustrum ovalifolium Hassk. California Privet	4	1	10-15	Semi	X		X		X		109
Ligustrum vulgare L. European Privet	2	1	8-15	Semi	X	X	XX		X		111
Myrica cerifera L. * Southern Waxmyrtle	3	3	6-30+	X	X		XX	X	X	X	113
Myrica pensylvanica Loisel. * Northern Bayberry	1	3	4-10	Semi		XX	XX	X	XX	XX	115

SPECIES	Resists Salt Windburn	Vigor of Growth	Average Height in feet	Ever-green	Good For:				General Use		See Page
					Clipped Hedges	Salt Wind Barrier	Screens	Bird Food	Land-scaping	Dune Erosion Control	
Nerium oleander L. Oleander	2	3	6-15	X	X		X		XX		118
Osmanthus americanus Benth & Hook. * Devilwood Osmanthus	2	4	8-20+	X					XX	X	120
Pittosporum tobira Ait. Tobira Pittosporum	1	2	6-10+	X	X	XX	XX		XX		122
Podocarpus macrophyllus Sieb. var. maki Shrubby Yew Podocarpus	3	4	6-20+	X	X		X		X		124
Raphiolepis umbellata Schneid. Yeddo Raphiolepis	1	4	4-8	X		X			XX		126
Rhus copallina L. * Flameleaf Sumac	3	1	4-10					X	X	X	127
Rosa banksiae R. Br. Banks Rose	3	2	1-4	X					X		130
Rosa rugosa Thunb. Rugosa Rose	2	2	4-6	X			X		XX	X	131
Rosa wichuraiana Crepin Memorial Rose	3	2	1-2	X					X	X	133
Ruscus aculeatus L. Butchersbroom	1	3	2-4	X		X			X		134

SPECIES	Resists Salt Windburn	Vigor of Growth	Average Height in feet	Ever-green	Good For:				General Use		See Page
					Clipped Hedges	Salt Wind Barrier	Screens	Bird Food	Land-scaping	Dune Erosion Control	
Tamarix gallica L. French Tamarisk, Saltcedar	1	2	8-12			X X	X		X	XX	137
Yucca aloifolia L. Spanish Dagger	1	4	6-12	X					XX	X	139
Yucca filamentosa L. * Adamsneedle, Beargrass	1	4	2	X		X			XX	X	140
Yucca gloriosa L. Moundlily Yucca	1	4	6-15	X					XX	X	140
Zanthoxylum clavaherculis L. * Herculesclub, Pricklyash	2	3	8-15			X	X	?	X	X	142
TREES Butia capitata Brazilian Butia (called Cocos australis at nurseries)	2	4	6-12	X					XX		143
Ilex opaca Ait. * American Holly	3	4	15-30	X				X	X		146
Juniperus virginiana L. * Eastern Redcedar	4	3	10-25	X			X	X	X	XX	148
Persea borbonia (L.) Spreng. * Redbay	3	3	10-40	X			X	X	X	X	150

SPECIES	Resists Salt Windburn	Vigor of Growth	Average Height in feet	Ever-green	Good For:				General Use		See Page
					Clipped Hedges	Salt Wind Barrier	Screens	Bird Food	Land scaping	Dune Erosion Control	
Pinus pinaster Ait. Cluster Pine	3	3	10-40	X					X		152
Pinus thunbergi Parl. Japanese Black Pine	3	3	10-40	X					XX		154
Populus alba L. White Poplar *	3	1	15-30						X		156
Prunus angustifolia Marsh. Chickasaw Plum *	3	2	4-8					X		X	159
Prunus caroliniana Ait. Carolina Laurelcherry *	3	3	10-20	X	X		X		X	X	160
Prunus serotina Ehrh. Black Cherry *	3	3	10-60					X	X		162
Quercus virginiana Mill. Live Oak *	3	4	6-40	X					X	XX	164
Sabal palmetto Lodd. ex Shultes Cabbage Palmetto *	2	4	15-30	X					XX		167
VINES											
Ampelopsis arborea (L.) Koehne Peppervine *	3	2						X	X	X	168

SPECIES	Resists Salt Windburn	Vigor of Growth	Average Height in feet	Ever-green	Good For:				General Use		See Page
					Clipped Hedges	Salt Wind Barrier	Screens	Bird Food	Land-scaping	Dune Erosion Control	
Campsis radicans (L.) Seem * Common Trumpetcreeper	3	2							X	X	170
Clematis paniculata Thun. Sweetautumn Clematis	3	2					X		X		172
Euonymus fortunei Wintercreeper (and varieties)	2	3		X					X		174
Gelsemium sempervirens (L.) Ait. f. * Carolina Jessamine	3	4		X					X	X	176
Lonicera sempervirens L. * Trumpet Honeysuckle	4	3		X					X		177
Parthenocissus quinquefolia (L.) Planch. * Virginia Creeper	2	2						X	X	XX	179
Smilax auriculata Walter. * Wild Bamboo	1	4		X		X		XX		XX	181
Vitis aestivalis Michx. * Summer Grape	2	3						X	X	XX	184
Vitis rotundifolia Michx. * Muscadine Grape	2	3						X	X	XX	186

SPECIES	Resists Salt Windburn	Vigor of Growth	Avg. Height in Feet	Ever-green	Good For				General Use		See Page
					Clipped Hedges	Salt Wind Barrier	Screens	Bird Food	Land-scaping	Dune Erosion Control	
HERBACEOUS PLANTS											
Artemisia stelleriana Bess. Dustymiller	1	4	1-2 1/2	X					XX		188
Cortaderia selloana Schult. (b) Selloa pampasgrass	3	2	5-8						X		190
Eryngium maritimum L. Seaholly Eryngo	1	3	1-2						X		191
Hemerocallis fulva L. Tawny Daylily	4	3	2-3						XX		193
Hydrocotyle bonariensis Lam. * Largeleaf Pennywort	1	2	1/2-1						X	XX	194
Hymenocallis calathina Nichols Basketflower	2	2	2 1/2						X		196
Iberis semperivirens L. Evergreen Candytuft	3	4	1	X					X		198
Lippia nodiflora (L.) Michx. * Lippia	1	2	1/2						X	X	199
Santolina chamaecyparissus L. Cypress Lavendercotton	1	4	1-1/2	X					XX		201

(b) For lawn grasses, see Section 4 - "Beach Landscaping"
For sand stabilization grasses, see Section 2 - "Stilling the Sand with Grasses and Forbs"

SECTION 6

PLANT DESCRIPTIONS

BACCHARIS HALIMIFOLIA

Eastern Baccharis, Saltmyrtle

DESCRIPTION - This is an open-growing brittle-branched, weedy shrub 3 to 11 feet tall. The leaves are thickened and usually coarsely toothed mostly toward the apex. A silvery sheen of fluffy, white flowers bloom and ripen in late fall. Each seed with its silky hair attachment is then scattered far and wide by the wind. The leaves are poisonous, and cattle have died after eating them.

Eastern baccharis (*Baccharis halimifolia*)
Holden Beach, North Carolina.

NOTES - Although this plant is number one in the table, it does not rate that high as a beach plant. This shrub prefers moist areas. It is found mostly in the "flats," marshes, and near the shorelines of sounds and estuaries. In many cases, it completely dominates such sites to the detriment of more useful vegetation. In waterfowl management work, it is considered a serious pest. But it has one over-riding good quality - it is almost impervious to ocean spray or even salt water flooding. It is moderately well adapted to much dryer sites and is found thinly scattered in dune valleys at a number of our beaches. It is quite common around cottages at Holden Beach, North Carolina. In South Carolina, the plant is called saltmyrtle. While the plant is not held in very high regard, it is well worth saving where it occurs naturally in dune areas.

CONSERVATION USE - The salt spray resistance of eastern baccharis can be put to good use as a front line wind barrier. A double row with plants 3 feet apart in each row will go a long way to protect less tolerant vegetation on the lee side. It is not a very good landscape subject even though it is quite attractive when in full bloom.

PROPAGATION - Plants are produced from seeds or cuttings of mature wood under glass.

Eastern baccharis in bloom

CALLICARPA AMERICANA

American Beautyberry

DESCRIPTION - A native deciduous shrub found in back areas where protected from salt winds. Habit of growth is upright, relatively unbranched, 3 to 6 feet tall, and about as wide. The leaves are in pairs opposite each other along the stems. They are soft textured, aromatic, 3 to 8 inches long, and 1 1/2 to 5 inches wide. Stems are straight and the plant has an open habit of growth. Bright lavender berries (drupes) are borne in tight clusters at regular intervals along the stems at the leaf axils. These appear in early September and are very showy even after the leaves have fallen. They remain on the plant until late winter; however, the color fades by late October.

American beautyberry (*Callicarpa americana*
Emerald Isle, North Carolina.

NOTES - The most abundant occurrence of American beautyberry was observed along the wooded section of highway between the Emerald Isle and Bogue Inlet fishing piers. Some of these shrubs are 6 feet tall. They grow best along the edge of the roadside. Here they are favored by the extra water which runs off the pavement and the additional light.

American beautyberry in fruit.

The plant is very drought resistant and seems to do quite well on poor sandy soil. It is moderately sensitive to salt spray. Therefore, beach plantings require wind protection.

The stems may be cut down to the ground in the spring after the berries have disappeared. This promotes sprouting. The new stems will fruit the same year.

The natural habit for beautyberry is in semi-shade of the forest or tree zone. At Folly Beach, South Carolina, a number of large specimens were found alongside a break in the frontal dune and within 100 feet of the ocean. At the Cape Hatteras lighthouse in North Carolina, it occurs as a flattened, wind-trimmed shrub behind the first dune.

CONSERVATION USE - This shrub may be used for beautification around buildings to show fall color of the berries. Evergreen shrubs are ideal for a background while red brick clashes. Plantings are placed on the lee side of buildings or other structural or vegetative barriers. It may be used in the shrub zone if other evergreen shrubs are already established to break the wind.

The berries, which persist into the winter, are choice food for cardinal, mockingbird, brown thrasher, wood thrush, and fair for bobwhite, catbird, and robin. (3)

PROPAGATION - American beautyberry is propagated by fall planting the cleaned seed or by taking cuttings which root readily in September.

CLEYERA JAPONICA

Cleyera

DESCRIPTION - An ornamental evergreen to about 8 feet; prized for its handsome, dark glossy foliage. The leathery leaves are lanceolate and long pointed at the lower end, veinless, and minutely toothed near the tips. The flowers, which appear in June, are creamy white and about 1/2 inch in diameter. Red fruits, which are two or three celled, ripen in the fall. The seeds are bright orange in color. The seed coating is oily.

Cleyera (*Cleyera japonica*). Charleston, South Carolina.

NOTES - Very little use has been made of this plant in beach areas. Most of the specimens found are at Myrtle Beach. The shining dark green foliage of this shrub is quite resistant to sea winds. These desirable characteristics should win more attention for cleyera along

Fruit of cleyera

Carolina beaches. Cleyera must be partially shielded from direct ocean wind. Some topsoil must be used in the transplant holes. Survival and growth will be increased with frequent watering.

CONSERVATION USE - This shrub is an excellent subject for beautification around beach homes and other buildings. It may be used alone as a specimen, in groups, shrub borders (4 to 5 feet spacing), or for more formal clipped hedges (2 to 2 1/2 feet spacing).

PROPAGATION - Nursery production is usually made by setting cuttings of the current year's growth in July through August. Plants are also secured by fall planting clean seed.

DAUBENTONIA PUNICEA

Rattlebox

DESCRIPTION - An open growing leguminous shrub to about 6 feet. The leaves are compound with the leaflets opposite each other along a central stem which is 4 to 8 inches long. Large sweetpea like flowers, orange-red in color, arise in loose clusters from the leaf bases of the outer branches. In the fall, four-angled seed pods 2 to 3 1/2 inches long are suspended on rather long appendages. These pods contain several hard coated, small bean-like seeds which are poisonous.

Rattlebox (*Daubentonia punicea*) growing in sand. Nags Head, North Carolina.

The four-angled seed pods of rattlebox.

NOTES - Being a legume, rattlebox gets an assist from nitrogen fixing bacteria on its roots. This enables the plant to grow on very poor soils including beach sands. It prefers a site where the water table is within easy reach of its root system.

The plant was originally brought in from South America. Since that time, it has spread northward along the Atlantic Coast and is planted mainly for the beauty of its very showy bloom.

CONSERVATION USE - Rattlebox will be of some use for dune stabilization work - expecially if it is planted in the flats between dunes. It will require at least this much protection from salt spray. Its nitrogen fixing characteristic may be of benefit to other plants with which it may be associated.

For beautification, it may be used as a single specimen. But it is much more impressive in groups or in rows for background. Because of its open growth habit, it is not at its best for foundation plantings. There is no record of its use by songbirds or other wildlife.

PROPAGATION - The seeds are used for increase. They are first cleaned, scarified (the seed coats scratched by rubbing between sheets of sandpaper) and then planted in nursery beds after danger of frost in the spring.

ELAEAGNUS PUNGENS

Thorny Elaeagnus

DESCRIPTION - This robust shrub will grow 6 to 11 feet tall and 5 to 10 feet wide. The leaves are evergreen and silvery underneath. Stems are also silvery and rusty brown on some varieties. Small fragrant flowers bloom in October and heavy crops of light red drupes speckled with silver mature in April. The fruit is about the size and shape of an olive seed. New growth first appears as elongated, spurred canes which are sparcely leaved. As leaves form and weight increases, these branches bend down to add to the height and spread of the shrub. If supported by the branches of a tree these canes become almost vine like and will climb to heights of 25 feet or more.

There are about a dozen varieties of this species. A few of the best and most common ones are varieties *reflexa*, *simoni*, and *fruitlandi*. All are vigorous, fast-growing shrubs.

NOTES - This species, like a legume, supports nitrogen fixing bacteria in the root hairs. This extra source of plant food enables the plant to endure on very poor sites.

Thorny elaeagnus (*Elaeagnus pungens*).
Nags Head, North Carolina.

We also note that it has exceptionally high resistance to salt spray. These important factors along with its year-around beauty and use by songbirds put this plant in an elite group of superior beach plants. My evaluation of this shrub is reflected by the shower of "brownie points" (X's) it received in the table in Section 5. It is especially popular at South Carolina beaches, where local nurserymen hold it in high regard. They often use it in plantings directly exposed to the ocean winds.

CONSERVATION USE - Thorny elaeagnus may be used in dune plantings, but its eventual requirements on these poor sands are in doubt. Initial test plantings have grown off well where some peat and fertilizer was incorporated with the sand. Refilling the planting holes with topsoil accomplished the same end.

The plant is very versatile when used in yards and around buildings and beach homes. As a clipped hedge (2 foot spacing) it requires frequent pruning. It is better as an untrimmed border or screen with 4 foot spacings and is superlative for salt wind barriers with plants 3 feet apart. If used as specimens or groups, they should be provided with plenty of room. The plants may be grown in medium to fairly dense shade.

The fruits ripen at a time when other songbird food is still scarce. Davison (3) lists it as a choice food of bluebird, mockingbird, thrasher, and towhee. The dense growth is a preferred nesting site for several species.

PROPAGATION - Elaeagnus may be propagated by cleaning the spring ripened seed and then planting in the field. A pine straw or other mulch is used on the nursery bed to promote germination and to prevent a disease which is generated from soil splashed on the small seedlings.

Nurserymen usually increase this plant by cuttings taken in late summer and fall. The use of indole-3-butyric acid on October cuttings raised the percentage of success from 72 percent (untreated) to 100 percent (5).

EUONYMUS JAPONICUS

Evergreen Euonymus

DESCRIPTION - An evergreen shrub with green stems 7 to 10 feet tall and 4 to 6 feet wide. The leaves are leathery, dark shining green and slightly serrated along the edges. The growth habit is irregular but upright. It has clusters of small creamy white flowers in spring and a four-seeded capsule which opens in late fall exposing the orange-red fruit. A variety (*E. japonicus aureo-variegatus*) has leaves which are marked with yellow. This variety does not have as much vigor as the common evergreen euonymus.

Evergreen euonymus *(Euonymus japonicus, aureo-variegatus)* trimmed against a cottage wall. Surfside Beach, South Carolina.

Evergreen euonymus in bloom.

NOTES - Euonymus is one of the five best adapted shrubs for beach conservation and beautification. It endures the direct buffeting of salt winds. In exposed positions heavy salt absorption by the plant often gives rise to abnormal accumulations of water in the plant tissues. The stems become turgid - often swollen to three times their normal diameter. Yet, this does not seem to adversely affect the plant's vigor and growth. Euonymus is bothered by scale and occasionally spider mites. If "clean" plants are brought to the beach, they tend to stay free of these pests.

The thickened stems of evergreen euonymus (*Euonymus japonica*) indicates salt absorption by the plant. Unusual defoliation of the shrub caused by unseasonably warm winter temperatures followed by a sharp drop to 13° F. on January 10, 1972. This plant survived. Emerald Isle, North Carolina.

Surprisingly, this versatile shrub has been used sparingly on the beaches. It has been observed most frequently in the Nags Head, Kill Devil Hill area in North Carolina. Perhaps its inland reputation of susceptibility to insect damage has put the "hex" on it. My experience with the plant at Emerald Isle has been entirely satisfactory. A row of potted stock planted in 1965 on an exposed yard area is now 7 feet tall.

CONSERVATION USE - For dune work, the planting site must be improved with topsoil, organic matter, and fertilizer.

If these requirements are practical, it is best used as a salt wind barrier with plants spaced 3 to 4 feet apart. It may also be spotted around in dune valley areas where its upright dark green foliage will accent less dramatic plant cover. For general beautification, it is fine for untrimmed shrub borders (4-foot spacing), trimmed hedges (2-foot spacing), for foundation planting where height is needed, and for groups or single specimens. However used, this shrub can be pruned to any shape or size.

The dark lustrous foliage is ideal in flower arrangements. With the orange-red berries, it is often used in Christmas decorations. The fruit has, in addition, food value for the bluebird, mockingbird, fox sparrow, and myrtle warbler.

PROPAGATION - Cuttings of half-ripened wood root easily. Long stems will root in a jar of water. Branches used in flower arrangements have rooted consistently for my wife. A large number of plants might be more easily handled by sowing clean seed in the fall. Seed may also be mixed with moist sand or peat moss, stored at 32° to 50° for three to four months, and then spring planted.

FATSHEDERA x LIZEI

Tree Ivy, Fatshedera

DESCRIPTION - This plant is a cross between English ivy and Japanese fatsia. It has beautiful, glossy evergreen leaves three to five lobed, starfish shaped, and up to 10 inches across. The habit is a semi-climbing, vine-like shrub to 9 feet. The stems are green. Long panicles of small greenish flowers bloom in the fall.

Tree Ivy
(*Fatshedera lizei*)

Tree ivy (right center). Charleston, South Carolina.

NOTES - Resistance to beach conditions is moderately good, but it must be well protected from whipping winds. Tree ivy will withstand a dry soil site, but not one which is poorly drained. It can take low winter temperatures but is less liable to cold damage if planted on a north exposure or in the shade.

CONSERVATION USE - For landscaping it must be supported against a building, wall, post, etc., and is excellent in this way as an espalier plant. It is also used in planter boxes, both in and out of doors.

PROPAGATION - Increases are made with cuttings of mature stems.

FATSIA JAPONICA

Japanese Fatsia

DESCRIPTION - Essentially a foliage plant with seven to nine finger-like lobes per leaf. The leaves are evergreen, leathery, up to 12 inches in diameter, and are distinctly tropical in appearance. The shrub can reach a height of 15 feet, but at the beach it is usually in the 3 to 6 foot category. The flowers are white in large branching panicles of multiple clusters 1 to 2 inches in diameter. The fruit is a light blue berry.

Japanese fatsia (*Fatsia japonica*)
Charleston, South Carolina.

NOTES - This plant likes shade. An hour or two of sunlight during the day meets its requirements. Once established, it needs little attention except occasional pruning to keep it compact in habit. It reportedly endures poor soil conditions and is partially resistant to salt spray. A beautiful specimen in Manteo, North Carolina, indicates its hardiness to this point.

CONSERVATION USE - A splendid landscaping plant because of its unique foliage. It must be well protected to prevent wind damage to the large leaves. Ideal for enclosed patio areas. Usually used as single specimens or small groups, but sometimes in borders where adequate protection is available.

PROPAGATION - Root cuttings are used to reproduce this plant.

HYDRANGEA MACROPHYLLA

Bigleaf Hydrangea

DESCRIPTION - This deciduous shrub has either pink or blue flowers at the stem ends in clusters up to 8 inches in diameter. The leaves are opposite, toothed along the edges, pointed, and up to 8 inches long. Although the plant can grow 8 feet tall, the usual height at the beach is 3 to 4 feet.

There are over 50 named varieties of this plant in the trade.

NOTES - In the South, bigleaf hydrangea is used both as a house plant as well as an outdoor landscape subject. It is used occasionally in gardens as far north as Cape Cod. Even so, one may expect some damage during abnormally cold snaps in northern latitudes of the North Carolina Coast. Usually, these large flowered hydrangeas produce blooms at the end of the terminal growth from buds formed the previous year. If branch tips are winter-nipped, few flowers will form.

Bigleaf hydrangea (*Hydrangea macrophylla*).
Salter Path, North Carolina.

The color of the flowers depends on the acidity of the soil. Acid soils produce blue flowers. The addition of lime or phosphate will turn the color of the flowers to pink.

It took imagination to move this plant to the beach since it does not appear to have the rugged qualities necessary for survival. Yet, it will grow successfully in the well drained sandy beach soils which have only a moderate amount of inherent fertility. It will not grow in the pure sands of dune soil and must be protected from whipping winds. Surprisingly, it will tolerate a fair amount of salt spray.

CONSERVATION USE - The showy flowers of this shrub have earned it a place in seaside landscaping. It is often used in foundation plantings where wind damage is minimized. In other sheltered spots it may be used for single specimens or in groups. Topsoil should be worked in around the roots.

PROPAGATION - Either half ripened or nearly ripe wood is used for cuttings under glass during the summer. Hardwood cuttings, layers, suckers, or division of older plants are also successful. Leafy softwood cuttings do well under mist. All respond markedly to indole-3-butyric acid treatment (16).

ILEX VOMITORIA

Yaupon Holly

DESCRIPTION - A native evergreen shrub to small tree 5 to 15 feet in height. The small inch-long leaves are leathery and dark green. Small greenish-white flowers, almost unnoticeable, appear in early spring. In the fall and winter, the charm of this plant lies in its abundant scarlett berries which cling closely to the branches of the previous year. The bark is gray and new twig ends purple. Occasional root suckers enable the plant to slowly increase. A dwarf and a weeping variety are available.

This species has the sexes separated - some plants are male and others, female. Thus, in the wild not all plants produce fruit.

Yaupon holly (*Ilex vomitoria*) wind sheared
Myrtle Beach, South Carolina

Yaupon holly in fruit

NOTES - This is one of our most beautiful native shrubs and is the most heavily fruited of all the hollies. It is best to use well developed stock in gallon cans or balled and burlapped. Nursery grown stock will be from cuttings taken from female trees. When transplanted, all of them will produce berries since in most locations wild male plants are nearby for pollination.

Yaupon is found in beach dune areas but mainly behind some protection from direct salt wind. Although the plant is recognized for its drought resistance, it is not especially resistant to salt burn. However, it is found in frontal areas on several beaches in South Carolina where exposure to the prevailing southwest wind is not as direct as on many North Carolina beaches.

CONSERVATION USE - The slow growth of yaupon holly not only makes it expensive to produce but also lengthens the time required for its establishment on dune sand. Therefore, it is not often recommended for wholesale application to dune sites. It may be used as an occasional group or specimen.

The bright red berries are used for Christmas decoration. They also are a choice food of the cedar waxwing and mockingbird, and its twiggy growth is often used for a nesting site. The leaves make good deer browse.

With some amendments to the sand and partial protection from sea wind, it is used to excellent advantage around beach homes as a clipped hedge, untrimmed screen or single or massed specimens. It may also be pruned to a tree-like form with one or more trunks. Conclusion - Yaupon is a very desirable and completely fitting part of any beach landscaping.

PROPAGATION - Yaupon holly is reproduced by cuttings of ripened wood taken from female plants. Seed may also be used, but they must remain in the ground for two years before germination and must then be cultivated for two years in the nursery before transplanting. Either way, production is somewhat tedious. Cuttings root with difficulty unless treated with root inducing naphthaleneacetic acid.

INDIGOFERA PSEUDOTINCTORIA

False Anil Indigo

DESCRIPTION - This is a low, shrubby perennial legume 1 to 2 feet tall and 2 to 3 feet wide. Fine profuse branching occurs at the crown to produce a dense procumbent growth. Leaves are fine and fern-like - somewhat resembling sericea lespedeza. Small sweetpea-like flowers lavender in color, start blooming in June and continue into mid-September. Small pea-like seed pods ripen at Emerald Isle, North Carolina, in early November. Frosts before this date will destroy most of the seed production.

False anil indigo (*Indigofera pseudotinctoria*) growing with Adamsneedle (*Yucca filamentosa*)

NOTES - This indigo is hardy at least to the Virginia line. It had the highest survival rate of 14 species planted in the dune test plantings at Ft. Macon and Hammocks Beach State Parks. It even survived and grew when planted directly in dune sand without any fertilizer or organic matter additives. This durability is partly explained by the fact that the plant is supplied with some plant food derived from nitrogen fixing bacteria which live in association with its roots. On Bogue Banks, North Carolina, plants will increase by volunteering from seed.

CONSERVATION USE - Indigo may be introduced into dune areas after the sand has been stilled by grass. If fertilized occasionally, it will not only improve the beauty, density, and permanence of the plant cover, but it may also furnish some nitrogen to promote grass growth to stabilize steep sand slopes (dune sides, banks, road cuts,

False anil indigo in bloom

etc.). Spacing in grass cover - 2 x 4 feet; on slopes, 16 x 16 inches.

For landscaping, it is best used in massed groups planted about a foot apart or in rows for low edging and borders and planted at the same spacing.

PROPAGATION - Increases of this plant are made by planting scarified seed in the spring. At the time of this writing, seed is not available commercially. Planting stock is available only in limited supply through district conservationists of the Soil Conservation Service or the plant materials specialist of the Soil Conservation Service in Raleigh, North Carolina. It is being introduced to local nurserymen in an effort to get it into commercial production.

IVA IMBRICATA

Marsh elder

DESCRIPTION - A low, perennial, native sub-shrub. It is sparsely branched with semi-woody stems more or less upright from ground level and 1 to 3 1/2 feet high. The leaves and stems are smooth without any pubescence. The fleshy leaves are narrow, lance shaped to about 2 1/4 inches long, but greatly reduced toward branch ends. The leaf edges are smooth or sometimes slightly toothed. Small, compact, greenish-yellow flower heads are borne along the main stems near the tops. In the fall, these contain several light brown nutlets more or less dull-pointed at one end and granular and aromatic when crushed between fingers.

Marsh elder has a strong system of rhizomes which allow it to spread and form colonies. In addition, roots develop along the stems if they are buried by sand.

Marsh elder (*Iva imbricata*)
Emerald Isle, North Carolina.

NOTES - This rugged plant is a familiar sight on coastal sand dunes. The thick fleshy leaves are impervious to salt spray and the plant is often found growing on beaches just above the high tide mark. Single plants spread upward and outward as sand accumulates around them. This produces a gently rounded dune of low stature. Such dunes are usually found in the youngest fore-ridge area of the beach.

A marsh elder seedling was found as the first pioneer plant on the cindery beach of a new island formed by recent volcanic action.

Seed heads of marsh elder

CONSERVATION USE - Marsh elder is regarded as a valuable dune conservation plant and recommended as such by Davis (10). Its complete adaptability to seaside conditions almost guarantees its usefulness - especially in the pioneer zone. However, it is not a good dune builder by itself. It is best regarded as a component in a mixture, usually with grass. In short, after a bare area has been stabilized with grass, marsh elder may be introduced as one of the long lasting perennials. Once established, it requires little to no maintenance.

Marsh elder may be used as a first "guard" row along the seaside edge of a salt wind barrier. It is sometimes seen as a natural part of the landscape plan around cottages.

PROPAGATION - Natural increases from seed commonly occur in the dune valleys around the old plants. These small first year seedlings transplant easily in the spring. Fifteen seedlings averaging 2 inches in height were transplanted and "watered in" on May 28, 1972. All survived. Dry seed planted in the spring failed to come. But seed collected, cleaned, and planted in the fall did well. In cleaning the seed care must be taken in rubbing away the chaffy bracts so as not to injure the fragile seed coats. The stems of established plants will root if buried by sand. Therefore, cuttings of the ripened stems should root readily.

JUNIPERUS CHINENSIS VAR. PFITZERIANA

Pfitzer Juniper

DESCRIPTION - A low, flat topped, evergreen shrub 3 to 5 feet tall, 5 to 8 feet wide. The foliage is similar to native red cedar. Needles are prickly with a bluish cast. Branches are mostly spreading, horizontal, loose, and graceful. The sexes are separate - the female plants have blue, berry-like fruits 3/8 inch in diameter which ripen the second year. This species does not creep and spread from rhizomes.

NOTES - Used sparingly in beach landscapes though it is apparently as well adapted as red cedar. It will endure poor unfertile sites but is susceptible to salt wind burn and must be used in protected areas - on the lee side of cottages, behind taller evergreens, screens, etc. They should be pruned annually to keep them from becoming open and straggly. Bagworms are a serious pest of all junipers and can completely defoliate a shrub. Malathion sprayed on infected shrubs will quickly correct the trouble. If only a few shrubs are involved, it is usually easier to pick the bagworms off by hand and drop them in a can of kerosene; or the kids can be slickered into picking them off - two for a penny.

Pfitzer juniper (*Juniperus chinensis* var. *pfitzeriana*)
Ocean Drive Beach, South Carolina

The seaside gardener will find that most of the shrub junipers handled by the nurseries in his area will be satisfactory at the beach. Like red cedar, they must be provided with sea wind protection. The best of these would be other varieties of *J. chinensis* as well as the low growing varieties of *J. horizontalis* - creeping juniper. (Also see *J. conferta* described elsewhere as a separate species.)

CONSERVATION USE - These junipers may be used for mass plantings or groups (with yucca as an example) and for borders and foundation plantings. In addition, the creeping *J. horizontalis* is especially good for low masses, low foreground plants in front of taller species, and bank cover. For complete ground cover protection, plant these 2 feet apart and mulch between.

PROPAGATION - These junipers are increased by taking hardwood cuttings during the fall and winter (September through December). Creeping juniper seems to root easier than Pfitzers. The use of sand-peat mixtures as a rooting medium is favored. Rooting was improved with the use of indole-3-butyric acid, especially for Pfitzers junipers

JUNIPERUS CONFERTA

Shore Juniper

DESCRIPTION - A semi-prostrate creeping shrub 1 to 2 feet tall and mat forming. It spreads vigorously from underground stems. If well fertilized, planted correctly, and mulched, it will make a full ground cover in two years. The needles are 1/2 to 1 inch in length, softer than red cedar, and are a pale greenish-blue in color. Small brown fruits are produced in the fall.

NOTES - As junipers go, this one is a fast grower. It is regularly recommended by nurserymen. Donald Wyman (2) describes this plant as "A low shrub for groundcover planting, especially adapted for planting on sand dunes in the vicinity of the seashore where other junipers cannot be grown successfully." This statement would seem to overrate the potential of *J. conferta* for dune stabilization work in the Carolinas.

A new and promising selection made by the Soil Conservation Service is 'Emerald Sea.' The mother stock was found along the seashore in Japan.

Shore juniper (*Juniperus conferta*)
Myrtle Beach, South Carolina

CONSERVATION USE - Many successful plantings have been observed around beach cottages and buildings where it is being used for mass, bank or border plantings, and often as a foreground in front of taller plant groups. Because of its lax and pliant stems it drapes over walls and planters with pleasing effect. But in all these situations, plantings had the benefit of partial wind protection. In addition, most had at least some topsoil around their roots. Modifying the site to fit this plant's needs is, however, well worth the trouble. Plant spacing is about 18 to 20 inches. Mulch between plants greatly accelerates establishment.

PROPAGATION - Shore juniper is propagated by taking cuttings from November through February and treating them with an indol-3-butyric acid solution.

*LIGUSTRUM JAPONICUM**

Japanese Privet

DESCRIPTION - A broadleaved evergreen shrub 5 to 10 feet tall with a spread of 4 to 6 feet. The leaves are leathery, oval shaped, dark green on top, light green below, opposite on the branches, and up to 4 inches long. Small white flowers are borne on terminal racemes in May. The blue-black fruits (drupes) ripen in November through December. Both flowers and fruit are conspicuous but not spectacular. The growth rate is fast. Privet belongs to the olive family.

Japanese privet (*Ligustrum japonicum*)
Nags Head, North Carolina

Japanese privet

NOTES - This is one of the most widely used landscaping plants on the beaches and in the Southeast generally. It will endure shade, and the leaves are not easily parched in hot dry weather or burned back by freezing. In the Myrtle Beach to Pawleys Island area in South Carolina, it is able to take the direct exposure to the ocean winds. In the Yaupon Beach to Ocean Isle and Atlantic Beach to Emerald Isle areas of North Carolina, it will take some damage in frontal areas and should be given partial protection or moved back and away from the most severe exposures.

CONSERVATION USE - Japanese privet is commonly used for trimmed hedges (2 foot spacing), unpruned shrub borders, and screens (3 to 4 foot spacing), and also as a subject for foundation plantings.

The shrubs are useful for bird nesting. It also supplies late winter food which is choice for purple finch, mockingbird, cedar waxwing, and fair for bluebird, cardinal, robin, and starling (3).

PROPAGATION - Privets are produced from fall sown seed or easily increased by cuttings taken in the summer (growing tips are best) or hardwood cuttings set in winter or early spring.

*A similar species is *Ligustrum lucidum* - tall glossy privet, which is taller (to 16 feet) and has larger and more pointed leaves than *L. japonicum*. Its coastal adaptation is probably good but unmeasured. The larger leaves are liable to greater damage by wind-whipping. In the nursery trade, *L. lucidum* is often called *L. japonicum* and vice versa.

*LIGUSTRUM OVALIFOLIUM**

California Privet

DESCRIPTION - This is a half evergreen, upright shrub to 15 feet tall and 8 to 10 feet wide. The leaves are 1 1/2 to 2 1/2 inches long, dark green and glossy above and yellowish green beneath. They usually take on a purple cast in late autumn. A compact panicle of small creamy white flowers about 3 inches long appear in May. Black berries ripen in the fall but the amount of fruiting is irregular. The plant is densely branched. The leaves and buds are not as resistant to salt winds as the leathery leaved Japanese privet.

California privet (*Ligustrum ovalifolium*)

Three privets: Amur, California, Japanese

NOTES - This quote is taken from L. H. Bailey's *The Standard Cyclopedia of Horticulture:* "*L. ovalifolium* is one of the best shrubs for seaside planting, growing well in the very spray of the salt-water." This enthusiastic observation is probably a California evaluation. In the Carolinas this plant, though well adapted climatically, is rare in beach plantings. It may deserve a more prominent place. In the Nags Head area and on the ocean side of two cottages, several plants were observed which were 5 feet tall and very wind worn. Potted plantings made just behind the frontal dune and also along the exposed side of a cottage at Emerald Isle promptly wind burned almost to the ground. They resprouted after brick windbreaks were set up to shield them. After these plants develop a deeper root system, they should give a better account of themselves.

CONSERVATION USE - Foliage of California privet is dense. Thus, they are best for clipped hedges. In this form, they have a solid wall-like appearance. Plant spacing for such a hedge is 16 to 20 inches. A distracting characteristic is the partial leaf drop in the winter. However, new leaves appear again very early in the spring.

PROPAGATION - This plant is easily propagated by taking cuttings of ripened wood most any time of the year. Winter hardwood cuttings may be buried over winter and set in the cutting beds or cultivated field rows in the spring.

*A similar semi-evergreen species with greater winter hardiness is *L. amurense,* Amur privet. Donald Wyman in *Shrubs and Vines for American Gardens* lists it and California privet as good beach plants. Carolina cottagers prefer Japanese privet by a wide margin.

LIGUSTRUM VULGARE

European Privet

DESCRIPTION - This shrub may usually be recognized by its numerous and strictly upright branches. It is a semi-evergreen plant to 15 feet. The leaves are opposite, leathery, oval to lance shaped, and up to 2 1/2 inches long. Loose pyramids of small white flowers appear in June on the terminal ends of the stems. A sparse crop of black lustrous berries ripen in October. Seed production of this species is light since the pollen bearing anthers of the flower remain deep in the corolla, while the pistil grows out and well above the corolla lip.

Two varieties are of special note: 'Pyramidale' with strictly upright branches but which tend to bend if left unclipped above 8 feet, and 'Densiflorum,' an upright growing clone, with a branching habit more dense than Pyramidale and which is less inclined to bend with height.

This species is a very vigorous grower.

NOTES - Some botanists contend that this plant is a native although its center of abundance is in Europe and west Asia. At any rate, it was also introduced to the eastern seaboard by early colonists.

A striking planting of *L. vulgare* is located at the old Fort Caswell, North Carolina. Here the shrubs show remarkable tolerance to salt sea winds. Japanese privet at the same location showed less vigor and some salt injury. These plantings are clipped back to 5 feet in height each spring. This produces a dense upright growth of long, vigorous sprouts, and indicates that the shrubs are probably one of the two varieties listed above.

European privet (*Ligustrum vulgare*)
Fort Caswell, North Carolina

CONSERVATION USE - This species may have possibilities but as yet is not recommended for dune revegetation. With the help of some topsoil around its roots and occasional fertilization, it should be useful for salt wind barriers, shrub borders, and screens (plant spacing 3 to 4 feet), or as clipped hedges (plant spacing 2 feet). Single untrimmed specimens are handsome; however, it is not a good subject for foundation planting where its tall vigorous growth would require much management.

PROPAGATION - Cuttings of this plant root easily if the ripened wood of the current year's growth is used.

MYRICA CERIFERA

Southern Waxmyrtle

DESCRIPTION - Southern waxmyrtle is a perennial, native, evergreen shrub usually 8 to 10 feet tall. In favored locations it may become a small tree to 36 feet. The leaves are leathery, yellowish green in color, and have a fresh aromatic odor when crushed. The spring blossoms are scarcely noticeable, but gray-white, wax-covered berries, 1/8 inch in diameter, appear in clusters on the old wood. These mature in late September and early October and are quite ornamental. This plant is dioecious - the male and female flowers are separated and occur on different plants of the same species. Waxmyrtle is not a legume. Yet, nitrogen bearing nodules are produced on its roots. This helps the plant to succeed on poor soil sites.

Waxmyrtle (*Myrica cerifera*) in a sand flat between dunes at Atlantic Beach, North Carolina.

Waxmyrtle with fruit

A variety of special interest to the soil conservationist is *M. cerifera* var. *pumila*. This is a colonial shrub to 3 feet tall which spreads from underground stems. Single plants sometimes cover an area of 20 feet or more in diameter. It seems better adapted to drier dune sites than *M. cerifera*. This variety is now under study at Soil Conservation Service plant materials centers. It is native to both the Carolinas.

NOTES - Southern waxmyrtle is at home in the "sand flats" areas of our coastal beaches. It prefers these moist locations which have a high water table. Since it is only moderately resistant to salt wind burn, it requires some windward protection. This is especially true in North Carolina. In South Carolina it is often found in more exposed positions.

CONSERVATION USE - The plant has value in dune revegetation work where its best use is on "sand flats" and in dune valleys. It may be planted in groups in the lower lying parts of an area. A spacing of 5 to 6 feet between plants is desirable.

The fruit remains on the bushes most of the winter and is a dependable source of food for birds. Verne Davison (3) notes that it is a choice food of the white-eyed vireo, myrtle warbler, and fair food for bobwhite, grackle, scrub jay, towhee, and red-bellied woodpecker. The dense evergreen branches also provide good nesting sites and wildlife cover.

The waxy fruits are still used to some extent in candle making. The "berries" are boiled in water. The wax comes to the top where it is removed and further refined.

This myrtle does well in landscaping around beach homes. Its texture is fine to medium; it combines well with junipers and makes a good background. For borders and screens, space plants 3 to 4 feet apart. As a single specimen, it is sometimes trimmed up as a small tree. In this form it is often used in restricted places (such as city malls) where a small tree is needed.

PROPAGATION - Seeds with the wax removed are planted in the fall. It is also increased by cuttings of ripened wood in the spring and summer or by layering. The suckers of *M. cerifera* var. *pumila* may be dug in early spring and transplanted. It would help to cut the rhizome attachment to the mother plant a year in advance to promote root development.

MYRICA PENSYLVANICA

Northern Bayberry

DESCRIPTION - A semi-evergreen shrub 3 to 8 feet tall with dark green elongated leaves 2 to 4 inches long, often notched above the middle and with a tiny point at the end. The sexes are separate - each plant being either male or female. The small inconspicuous bayberry flowers in spring are followed by wax covered gray-white berries on female plants in late September. These berries (actually nutlets) are about 5/32 of an inch in diameter and noticeably larger than those of wax myrtle. They appear in clusters on the old wood. The fruit and leaves of bayberry have a fresh aromatic odor. The fruit remains on the stems over winter. Bayberry spreads slowly by means of short rhizomes to form colonies. Its growth on poor soil sites is aided considerably by nitrogen bearing nodules on its roots - a factor which contributes heavily to its high rating as a beach plant. An interesting variety which is evidently a natural cross of this species with *Myrica cerifera* is *Myrica macfarlanei*. This plant is shorter in stature to about 3 feet and is noted for its excellent spread from rhizomes. The growth rate of bayberry is moderate.

Bayberry (*Myrica pensylvanica*)
Kitty Hawk, North Carolina

The female bayberry plant with fruit
Emerald Isle, North Carolina

NOTES - Bayberry ranges chiefly along the coast from about Cape Hatteras, North Carolina, northward. A very successful five year old test planting at Emerald Isle, North Carolina, proves that it is well adapted to this point. Other Soil Conservation Service test plantings established in the spring of 1971 on the beach near Georgetown and Charleston, South Carolina, grew well in their first season. This strengthens our belief that this extremely valuable beach species will find a useful place in South Carolina.

Bayberry is highly resistant to salt spray. It is found in every variety of situation and soil from the dry sandy dunes to the border of marshes. Lucius D. Davis in *Ornamental Shrubs* says, "This little shrub when planted along the shore withstands the ocean winds and storms perhaps better than any other plant known in cultivation .... Almost any bleak and barren exposure can be covered in this way and become comparatively beautiful."

CONSERVATION USE - The greatest potential use for bayberry is for sand dune stabilization where the sand has been stilled by American beachgrass plantings or other native grass cover. Where climatically adapted, it is certainly one of the best plants for this purpose.

For ornamental use, the whitish berries have an interesting effect when exposed in the winter. These fruit-laden twigs are sometimes stripped of leaves and sold for use in floral arrangements. The waxy fruit is also collected to some extent for candle making in the northeast.

In beach beautification work, bayberry has a medium texture. It is good for background or border, and superb in a row (2 to 3 feet spacing) as a salt wind barrier to shield less resistant vegetation. The occasional sprouts are never a problem in lawns and are easily controlled elsewhere by an occasional chopping.

F. C. Edminster and R. M. May in the USDA Circular 887, *Shrub Plantings for Soil Conservation Wildlife Cover in the Northeast,* claim that this shrub is "one of the best for improving cover and food conditions for wildlife. The fruit is a staple food for the bobwhite and ruffed grouse and is readily eaten also by the ring-necked pheasant, wild turkey, and at least 35 kinds of songbirds."

PROPAGATION - The easiest way to propagate bayberry is to remove the waxy seed covering and plant the clean seed in the fall. It is also increased by cuttings of ripened wood in the fall and by transplanting the sprouts.

NERIUM OLEANDER

Oleander

DESCRIPTION - Oleander is a very straight stemmed upright shrub. The stems as well as the leaves remain green over winter. Height varies from 6 to about 15 feet but in beach areas usually less than 10 feet. The narrow, leathery leaves occur in whorls of three, rarely four or two. The several varieties produce white, yellow, red, or purple flowers which are salver-shaped, 3 inches in diameter, and are single or double. The red flowered variety is the most cold hardy. The flowering period is June and July, and the beautiful display makes this plant a favorite of southern gardeners. The seed are borne in long pencil-shaped pods.

Oleander (*Nerium oleander*)
Sullivans Island, South Carolina

Oleander in bloom

NOTES - The leaves and flowers of oleander are poisonous if eaten by man or beast. Smoke from burning oleander trash can be dangerous.

Oleander is a very popular landscaping plant especially on South Carolina beaches. It has high salt wind resistance having a "two" rating in our table. It reaches optimum growing conditions in the vicinity of Charleston and south and 10 to 12 foot specimens are found around the old homes on Sullivans Island. The plant ranges along the coast as far north as Virginia. But in the area roughly north of Wilmington, North Carolina, it should be given some protection from the cold northern exposure. Use of the red flowered variety in these more northerly plantings will also help to assure success.

This shrub sprouts very freely, so it can withstand harsh pruning. It may be kept at most any height and pruning favors flowering. Scale which sometimes attacks this plant can be controlled with an oil spray; mealy bugs can be dispatched with a garden hose.

Oleander was severely injured during the winter of 1970 - 1971. The damage was due to unusually late warm weather in the fall followed by sudden hard freezes. Some cottagers mistakenly attributed the trouble to salt spray. Actually, this species was cold hurt from North Carolina to north Florida during this period.

CONSERVATION USE - Oleander has not been tested for dune stabilization work although Davis (10) recommends such trials. It does have a South Carolina reputation of growing "anywhere." It is useful for borders, salt wind barriers, backgrounds, and screens with a plant spacing of 3 to 4 feet. Single specimens are very ornamental and where some height is needed, it may be used in foundation plantings.

PROPAGATION - The plant may be propagated by cuttings of mature summer wood stuck in July or August after flowering. Stems may be rooted if placed in a jar of water. Also, seed can be collected in late fall. Most of the fuzzy coating is removed by rubbing through a coarse wire mesh. The seed are then planted immediately in greenhouse flats. Germination occurs in about two weeks. (16).

OSMANTHUS AMERICANUS

Devilwood Osmanthus, Wild Olive

DESCRIPTION - Wild olive (the name I prefer) is a native evergreen shrub or small tree which grows to a height of 20 feet or more. The leathery leaves are oblong to about 4 inches, blunt tipped, glossy green, and distinctly rolled along the edges. The bark is gray. Flowers are small, white, and very fragrant. They occur in clusters along the stems at the base of the leaves. In the fall, dark blue, olive-like single-seeded fruits are produced. The growth is not dense. This plant occurs in the Coastal Plain and ranges from North Carolina to Florida. The growth rate is slow.

NOTES - Wild olive grows well in the deep sands of coastal dune areas. The leaves have very good salt wind resistance. These two facts, coupled with its pleasing fragrance and year-around beauty, earn it a high rating as a beach plant. In dune areas, it is found with yaupon holly, live oak, cedar, etc., where it grows in the form of a flat-topped shrub. In back areas with more protection, it becomes a small tree 15 to 20 feet or more in height.

Devilwood osmanthus or wild olive (*Osmanthus americana*).
Fruit at upper right. Atlantic Beach, North Carolina.

Leaves of devilwood osmanthus.

CONSERVATION USE - This plant would seem to be a good subject for dune revegetation work. Unfortunately, propagation is difficult. Large-scale use of the plant for this purpose would be expensive and probably impractical. A few plants used in small groups for contrast would be appropriate.

For landscaping, its open growth and handsome foliage is ideal as a single specimen or as a central plant in a group of lower growing species. Interesting results can also be had by pruning to the form of a small tree. Such a specimen will grow to a good height if planted on the lee side of a building.

PROPAGATION - Increases are made by cuttings of half-ripened wood in late summer. The cuttings are not easy to root. Seeds are rather difficult to come by since production is erratic and not prolific. In addition, seeds do not germinate until the second year.

Although inquiries were made at a number of coastal nurseries, no commercial production of wild olive was found. It should gain in use as its rugged adaptability to beach conditions becomes better known.

PITTOSPORUM TOBIRA

Tobira Pittosporum, Pittosporum

DESCRIPTION - An evergreen shrub to 10 feet with leathery, lustrous, dark green leaves. They are oblong finger shaped to 4 inches with the edges more or less rolled inward. Clusters of creamy white flowers, somewhat resembling orange blossoms in color and fragrance, bloom in April and May. The fruit, which is an angular capsule, matures in late October or early November. The several seeds in each capsule are orange in color and covered with a glue-like substance which nature has provided to promote the spread of the seed by birds.

General growth of the shrub is stiff and bushy with an interesting, though not particularly dense, branch system. Growth rate is moderate to fast. The leaves of the variety *P. tobira* var. *variegatum* are pale bluish-green edged with white. It is not as vigorous nor as beautiful as the common species.

Tobira pittosporum (*Pittosporum tobira*)
Nags Head, North Carolina

NOTES - This handsome shrub, in my opinion, is the queen of all beach landscaping plants in the Carolinas. This is verified by the great number of beach residents who have included it in their plantings. The reason for this popularity is its near perfect performance in withstanding the violent saline winds, its fragrant flowers and lustrous dark green beauty, and its ease of cultivation. This is one of the few plants which can prosper on sites directly exposed to the sea winds in the rugged Atlantic Beach - Emerald Isle area in North Carolina.

Pittosporum (accent on the "tos" if you wish to be correct!) prefers a loose, well-drained soil. Topsoil mixed with the beach sand seems to be an ideal combination. Another feature of this versatile plant is its ability to thrive in either full sun or almost complete shade. Once established, it responds quickly to fertilization. Extra nitrogen will turn its leaves to a waxy deep green.

CONSERVATION USE - For general use around buildings, this shrub is at its best for salt wind barriers (3 foot spacing), tall backgrounds, shrub borders and screens (4 foot spacings), or as individual specimens. If shearing is started early, these plants spaced 2 feet apart can be used for hedges. However, Japanese or California privet are superior for clipped hedges since both are more leafy and densely branched.

If plants are to be used as a windbreak to protect other vegetation, pittosporum would be a good choice.

PROPAGATION - Pittosporum is easily propagated by fall planting the seed. The seeds are first rubbed in dry beach sand to separate them, or rubbed between rough cloth to reduce the stickiness, and then covered with talc. In an effort to dissolve the sticky seed coating, I have tried water, soap and water, varsol, alcohol, and lacquer thinner - all to no avail. The lacquer solvent softened the substance to a point where it was more easily rubbed off. Cuttings of half-ripened wood taken in midsummer will also root quite readily. Success is increased by treating the cuttings with indole-3-butyric acid and placing them under mist (16).

PODOCARPUS MACROPHYLLUS var. *MAKI*

Shrubby Yew Podocarpus

DESCRIPTION - This native of Japan is a pyramidal shrub 8 to 10 feet tall and 3 to 5 feet wide. Branches and leaves are somewhat upright. The needle-like evergreen leaves are 1 3/4 to 3 inches long, 1/5 to 1/4 inch wide, dark green with a prominent midrib on the upper surface, and pale green beneath. Seed are oval shaped, 1/3 to 1/2 inch long, borne in tandem with a fleshy purplish receptacle. They are poisonous. Growth rate is slow.

Shrubby Yew Podocarpus (*Podocarpus macrophyllus* var. *Maki*)
Myrtle Beach, South Carolina

NOTES - Yew podocarpus does have a cold hardiness limitation. Plantings north of Wilmington may do somewhat better if sheltered from the cold north wind. Direct sea winds will "burn" it even in the "Grand Strand" area. Yet, it occurs quite frequently along South Carolina beaches, especially in the more recent and elaborate motel plantings. The plant withstands pruning very well, and the fine texture lends itself to clipping and shaping.

CONSERVATION USE - This is a very decorative plant especially for clipped hedges (2 to 2 1/2 foot spacing) or untrimmed shrub borders (3 to 4 foot spacing). An individual plant may be sheared to any shape or left to assume its natural form as a specimen or as a component of plant groups.

PROPAGATION - The seeds may be gathered and planted before the fleshy section has dried. Increases are also made by taking cuttings of mature wood in October through November.

RAPHIOLEPIS UMBELLATA

Yeddo Raphiolepis*

DESCRIPTION - A compact globe-shaped evergreen shrub to 8 feet. The leaves are leathery, almost round to oval shaped, and 1 1/2 to 2 1/2 inches long. White flowers 3/4 inch in size appear in loose clusters in the spring. There is a dwarf variety which is less than 16 inches tall. In the fall, dark blue-black fruits about half the size of a ripe olive are borne in profusion at the branch tips. These contain one, sometimes two, compressed seeds. This plant is well behaved with not one branch willing to outgrow any other.

Yeddo raphiolepis (*Raphiolepis umbellata*) surrounded by pittosporum. Atlantic Beach, North Carolina

Raphiolepis umbellata

NOTES - Though not a front runner in quantities used, it is fairly well distributed on all our beaches. Most nurserymen have a kind word for its form, size, and texture which has given them a shrub for definite contrast. It is also regarded as invincible when pitted against salty sea winds. These excellent qualities give this shrub a very high rating for beach work.

The growth rate is slow. It prefers a loose, well drained soil which it gets when beach sand is mixed with topsoil.

CONSERVATION USE - In the landscape, it is used for foundation plantings, borders, or groups most often with taller shrubs in the background. It is good under windows where it is easy to maintain below the sill level.

PROPAGATION - Seeds with skins removed are planted in the fall. Cuttings of ripened wood are also used. It may also be increased by layering - bending a branch down and covering part of the stem with soil held firmly in place with a brick.

*This species is commonly called Indian hawthorne.

RHUS COPALLINA

Flameleaf Sumac

DESCRIPTION - This sumac is a native shrub to small tree and is found on many of the poorest acid soils in the Southeast. It is deciduous, but the leaves go out with a scarlet blaze of glory in the fall. The leaves are compound or fern-like with usually 9 to 11 leaflets. These are very shiny on top and their central stems are winged or flanged with a narrow margin of leaf tissue along each side. For this reason, the species is sometimes called "winged" sumac. This species is dioecious - each plant produces only male or female flowers. The loose cone-shaped panicles of small greenish or cream colored flowers bloom in July and August. The female plants produce clusters of red, hairy-coated seeds at the tip end of the branches. These clusters add to the fall beauty of the plant. The underground system tends to put out one or two lead "roots" which ramble - putting up occasional sprouts as they go. Thus, if left undisturbed, a single plant will spread to make a colony. The form of such a colony is usually a series of bare stems arising from the ground with an umbrella of leaves and fruiting parts at the top.

Flameleaf sumac (*Rhus copallina*)
with seed head

A sumac plant from a 5-inch root cutting.

NOTES - Flameleaf sumac has a tolerance for poor droughty soils, but it actually prefers a moist site. In dune planting tests near Fort Macon and Hammocks Beach State Parks, its survival rate ranked very high in the flatter dune valleys.

The thin walled leaves are more susceptible to salt windburn and simple parching than many of the evergreen types with thick leathery leaves.

Its spread from rhizomes is a valuable asset in this work. The sprouts are not troublesome in lawns or other areas where their increase is not desired. Lawn mowing completely obliterates them, and elsewhere occasional shoots can easily be pulled out.

CONSERVATION USE - Davis (10) suggests that this plant ought to be useful in dune erosion control work. The ability to succeed on moderately dry sites and its occasional presence in the shrub zone would justify this opinion. Due to its tendency to salt burn, it would best be tried in dune valleys or with other more tolerant plants for protection. Plant spacing of 6 to 8 feet would provide a good start.

Its beauty and unique form should not be overlooked in landscaping especially if it is trained into palm tree-like forms. Mass plantings would also have good esthetic quality in the fall. The seed are oily coated and quite acid. In spite of this, the fruit, which holds on late into the winter, is an important bird food - choice for catbird, and fair for bluebird, mockingbird, robin, starling, hermit thrush, turkey, and red-headed woodpecker (3).

PROPAGATION - This plant is increased by cleaning the seed, scarifying it for one hour with a coating of sulphuric acid, and then planting it in the fall. Smaller numbers of plants may be secured from root cuttings put out in the spring. The cable-like roots are cut in 4 to 6 inch lengths and planted 3 inches deep in the sand, or half that depth if planted in topsoil.

ROSA BANKSIAE

Banks Rose

DESCRIPTION - A semi-evergreen rambler which will climb to 15 feet or more. Without a support, the plant is at first upright to about 5 feet. The long arching branches then bend and trail on the ground. The green stems are smooth and thornless. Leaves are shining green and finely toothed. Flowers, double or single, yellow (sometimes white), and about one inch across, are borne in clusters. The plant is a very fast grower.

Banks rose (*Rosa banksiae*)

NOTES - This one is listed by nurserymen as an adapted seaside plant but only a few specimens are found. These indicated moderate to good tolerance to salt spray. It may be trained over walls or on a trellis. If planted near supporting vegetation, it will climb over shrubs and to the tops of trees.

CONSERVATION USE - This rose is untested for dune stabilization, but its long weeping stems indicate potential for this use. Gardners use the plant for its attractive yellow flowers and the pleasing appearance of its green stems in winter.

PROPAGATION - This rose is produced by cuttings of new wood taken in early summer. It is more difficult to root than most roses.

ROSA RUGOSA

Rugosa Rose

DESCRIPTION - A shrub upright to 6 feet, stems stout, densely bristly, and prickly. Each leaf has five to nine firm, dark, lustrous leaflets, 3/4 to 2 inches long, serrate along the edges, and somewhat hairy beneath. The plants bloom all summer. The flowers are solitary, 2 to 2 1/2 inches across, bristly, and short stemmed. In the fall, the hips are round, smooth, brick red, and up to 1 inch across. The autumn color of its foliage is a brilliant orange. Root suckers enable the plant to increase slowly in size.

Forms of typical *R. rugosa* are varieties: *alba* with white flowers, *albo-plena* with double white flowers, *rosea* with pink flowers, *rubra* with purple flowers, and *rubro-plena* with double purple flowers.

Rugosa rose (*Rosa rugosa*)
Kill Devil Hill, North Carolina

Rugosa rose

NOTES - This was one of the five most successful shrubs in a Soil Conservation Service seashore dune planting project in New Jersey. The plant is adapted in the Carolinas, but the only specimens found were in the Nags Head area. Rugosa rose has better than average resistance to salt burn and has good potential as a dune protection plant. The large hips have some value for wildlife food and are also ornamental. Wyman (1) says, "It is impossible to say too much in favor of this 'sea tomato' of Japan, so called because in its native habitat it grows within reach of the salt water spray."

CONSERVATION USE - Time will tell whether or not *Rugosa rose* will persist as permanent cover for dunes. The sand of the planting sites must be improved to secure establishment, but after that, further management necessities are still unknown. In dune planting tests it has an excellent first year survival rate and moderate growth.

The shrub will make an impenetrable border with a plant spacing of 2 feet or with a wider spacing to give each plant more definition. As a formal hedge it withstands clipping well.

The texture is medium with a rather open habit. Its dark lustrous leaves form a good background border.

PROPAGATION - Stock is produced from cuttings of mature wood stored over winter in cool sand and planted outside in the spring. Softwood cuttings taken in June, July, and August will do well under glass. Indole-3-butyric acid will speed the rooting of most rose cuttings (5). Stock is also produced by planting clean seed in the fall or stratified seed (30 days in damp peat or sand at 36° to 40°) in the spring.

ROSA WICHURAIANA

Wichura Rose, Memorial Rose

DESCRIPTION - A partly evergreen vine-like shrub with long trailing stems sometimes to 20 feet or more. The stems have strong, curved, solitary prickles. Leaves are dark green and composed of seven to nine roundish leaflets 1/3 to 3/4 inch long and coarsely serrate along the margins. The white, single petaled flowers are 1 1/2 to 2 inches wide. Hips are oval shaped, red colored, and about 1/2 inch long. The prostrate stems grow rapidly and take root where covered with soil.

Wichura rose (*Rosa wichuraiana*) on a steep bank.

NOTES - Wichura rose is somewhat sensitive to salt spray and must be partly shielded from the direct ocean wind. While the vines reach out rapidly, it takes several years to establish full ground cover.

CONSERVATION USE - This shrub has long been famous as a ground cover for infertile, dry, rocky, or sandy sites. Observations were made of a single occurrence of this

Wichura rose blooms

plant at Emerald Isle, North Carolina. But Wyman (1)(2) also lists it as a good seashore plant. It may do well between dunes for erosion and foot traffic control if proper soil amendments are made.

The texture of these plants is quite fine. Its main landscaping use is for ground cover. If trained on fences, it makes an admirable screen.

PROPAGATION - This rose is produced by planting clean seed in the fall or by hard or semi-hardwood cuttings taken in late summer or fall. Six-inch hardwood cuttings may be planted outside in rows during October. They are placed upright so that the tops are flush with the ground. A light loamy or sandy soil gives best results. Such cuttings will sprout and produce some leaves before cold weather.

RUSCUS ACULEATUS

Butchersbroom

DESCRIPTION - Butchersbroom is a unique conservation piece. The foliage, or at least what looks like the leaves, is actually flat-bladed extensions of the branches. These pseudo-leaves, 1/2 to 1 1/2 inches long, are leathery, evergreen, and taper to a spiny point. The plant is dioecious. Flowers are very small and closely attached to the upper central section of the so called leaves. The blooms appear in November. The dark purple centers are surrounded by three tiny, greenish petals. Female plants produce red berries about 1/2 inch in diameter. The branches are stiff and up to 3 feet tall. A few of them die back each year and new ones sprout from the ground to take their place. The plant spreads slowly by means of this sprouting from the roots.

Butchersbroom (*Ruscus aculeatus*)

NOTES - This is well known as a seacoast plant in south and western Europe. It is equally well adapted along our coast in the South and up through eastern Virginia. Webster (16) says: "As a seaside woodland shrub the butchersbroom produces its bright pink fruit in abundance and, being of evergreen character, lights up a deciduous woodland during the dull winter season. Recommended as underwood in all seaside plantations." Menninger (13) notes that this shrub may be used in the "front line" close to the ocean.

The small spine-tipped leaves of butchersbroom

This species is rare along the Carolina beaches. It is listed as "half-hardy" as far as cold is concerned. There are several specimens in Raleigh, North Carolina.

CONSERVATION USE - The salt resistance of this plant suggests its use with salt wind barriers. Its spine tipped leaves may be used to advantage in plantings which control or prohibit foot traffic.

The low evergreen growth coupled with the beauty of winter berries suggest many landscape uses, especially in foundation plantings and borders. The green branches are excellent for Christmas arrangements with the red berries of other species.

PROPAGATION - Increases are made by division. Information on use of its seed has not been found.

TAMARIX GALLICA

French Tamarisk, Saltcedar

DESCRIPTION - Here's an import from the western United States where it is thoroughly despised for its greedy, water seeking roots. It originally came from the Eurasian area. The plant is a deciduous shrub 8 to 10 feet tall. Small scale-like leaves, blue-green in color, give it a feathery appearance. Small spikes of tiny white or pink flowers show up at the tips of branches in May to July. They rarely set seed in this area.

The bark is smooth and cinnamon-brown in color. Branching is completely haphazard with stems growing every which way. Thus, the shrub has a poor but generally upright form.

There are also several other well adapted species. A few of the better ones are: *T. hispida,* Kashgar tamarisk to 4 feet; *T. odessana,* odessa tamarisk to 6 feet; *T. parviflora,* smallflower tamarisk to 15 feet; and *T. pentandra,* fivestamen tamarisk to 15 feet.

Saltcedar (*Tamarix gallica*)
Sullivans Island, South Carolina

Saltcedar blooms

NOTES - Saltcedar is quite abundant in the Wrightsville Beach area. The "mother plant" may well be a large specimen at the southern tip of the island where it has built up a dune 40 feet or more long and about 8 feet high. Main stems buried by drifting sand sprout new roots and the shrub continues to grow upward as the sand accumulates around it. After its far-ranging roots have reached water, the plant is resistant to salt spray and strong winds.

CONSERVATION USE - Saltcedar would seem to have a useful future for erosion control in seaward dune valleys and especially "flats" where moisture prevails. In these situations, it may be used in groups or in rows for salt spray barriers (3 x 3 foot spacing). It is possible to use unrooted cuttings in these places. In landscaping, it should not be used for foundation plantings where its supple branches, whipping in the wind, will wear out anything within reach (including the paint on a cottage!). Its principal value as an ornamental is its fine feathery foliage which can be used for an effective change in texture or to soften harsh lines. Pruning may be severe since saltcedar sprouts prolifically.

PROPAGATION - An interesting feature of saltcedar is the method by which it may be propagated. Whips which are 12 to 16 inches long and 1/4 to 3/4 of an inch thick may be cut in late March and inserted two-thirds their length in the beach sand. They are "watered in" to bring the sand in close contact with the stem. Such plantings usually have a high rate of survival - especially if watered occasionally until rooted. A good site for such cuttings is under the drip of a cottage roof.

YUCCA ALOIFOLIA

Spanish Dagger

DESCRIPTION - The leaves of Spanish dagger are stiff, tapered, dagger-like, and sharp pointed from a central crown at the ground, later forming a stocky trunk to 10 feet or more. Leaves have smooth margins and are up to about 1 3/4 inches wide. Bottom leaves die off as the trunk lengthens. Creamy, bell-shaped flowers appear in June and July on a tall central stem. In October through December they produce heavy blackish-purple fruits about 3 1/2 inches long and filled with black, moist, swollen seed. (See NOTES below)

Yuccas marching down to the sea.
Myrtle Beach, South Carolina

YUCCA FILAMENTOSA

Adamsneedle, Beargrass

DESCRIPTION - Bold, stiff, light green leaves from the ground in a tuft 1 to 2 feet tall, with curly threads attached and hanging along leaf edges. White bell-like flowers bloom on a tall central stem in May and June. The fruit ripens in September and October. The seed capsules are about 2 inches long and tightly packed with flat black seeds.

This plant spreads slowly from tubers to form an everwidening clump. It may develop a very short trunk, but this is usually absent. Also, a variety, *Y. filamentosa concava*, has broad, stiff, spoon-like leaves. (See NOTES below)

YUCCA GLORIOSA

Moundlily Yucca

DESCRIPTION - This one is very similar to *Y. aloifolia* in its habit of growth. It develops a trunk, sometimes 15 feet. The leaves are up to 2 3/8 inches wide with roughened margins. The plant blooms in October. Flowers are sometimes tinged with red. The fruit ripens in November and December. Seeds are flattened and packed tightly in the drooping capsule. (See NOTES below)

NOTES - All following information will apply to the three species of Yucca described above: Yuccas are used extensively for beach beautification. In this respect, they rank in the top three in frequency of occurrence. Their appearance is striking. They are exclamation points which accentuate the vast difference between the beach and inland environments.

YUCCAS thrive on poor, dry sand dune soil and are almost impervious to windblown salt spray. Some leaf tips occasionally "burn" on fully exposed sites. The plants will volunteer in dune lands where sand drift has been controlled. Yuccas transplant easily. Survival is best when two-thirds of the bottom green leaves are clipped off after planting. Rotting is induced if the base of any of the living leaves are placed below ground level. Depth of plantings is especially important with beargrass.

Beargrass or Adamsneedle (*Yucca filamentosa)*
showing curly threads along leaf margins.

CONSERVATION USE - Yucca is not a good sand stilling plant namely in that it places no great restrictions on the wind. Yet its presence in dune plantings adds diversity and contrast. Rows of yuccas are sometimes used to divert or restrict foot traffic. Adamsneedle (or beargrass) planted in this manner makes formidable first line of defense in salt wind barriers.

In landscape work, they are usually used in groups or in rows along borders, walks, roads, etc. For those species with trunks, the lower leaves may be hacksawed off, leaving a tuft of the younger leaves at the top. This gives the effect of a miniature palm. Ground cover plants or landscape gravel may be used under such specimens.

Tall yuccas (*Y. aloifolia* and *Y. gloriosa*) may be mixed with or placed behind the trunkless beargrass (*Y. filamentosa*.) It is important to remember that the first two above are sharp pointed and can be dangerous. They should be planted back or away from walks, doorways, and other areas where foot traffic is not to be restricted. To add to their beauty, all dead or badly damaged lower leaves should be cut off close to the trunk each year.

PROPAGATION - Yuccas are propagated by seed, or in the case of *Y. filamentosa* by dividing the growing clumps. All species transplant easily. The tops of tall growing types may be cut off in 2 to 3 foot lengths and used for propagation. The butt ends are trimmed off leaves and planted about a foot deep.

ZANTHOXYLUM CLAVA-HERCULIS

Herculesclub, Pricklyash

DESCRIPTION - A stout spined, deciduous shrub to small tree which is native to the Carolina coastline. It sometimes reaches a height of 18 feet but in beach areas usually less than 12 feet. The leaves are compound, semi-evergreen, and 5 to 8 inches long with 7 to 17 leathery, shallowly toothed leaflets. The mainstem of the leaf is often armed with thorns. The leaflets are aromatic, lustrous above, somewhat twisted, and the mid vein of each is off-center (closer to the lower margin). Flowers bloom in April and May in terminal panicles, and the seeds are shiny black, round, about 1/8 inch in diameter, and quite oily. The bark of the trunk is barely 1/16 of an inch thick, light gray and roughened by corky tubercles. The plant spreads slowly from widely spaced root sprouts.

Herculesclub (*Zanthoxylum clava-herculis*)
Fort Macon, North Carolina

NOTES - A strong point in favor of this plant is its ability to thrive on dune sand. It is not abundant and is found only along the coastal area. It has a salt wind resistance rating of "2" which is a strong indication of its potential usefulness. However, in dune areas close to the ocean, it is usually trimmed to a shrub form. Old timers claim that chewing the aromatic leaves or bark will alleviate a toothache. In some localities it is known as the "toothache tree." The heavy bloom of flowers in the spring attract many bees and it is known as a good honey plant.

CONSERVATION USE - This plant has good potential for dune revegetation work, at least in mixture or in groups with other woody perennials. The armed branches will also be effective in directing or inhibiting unwanted foot traffic in the dunes.

As a plant for decorative uses, it has an open habit, coarse texture, and informal shape. The corky projections on the branches and trunk give the plant an unique winter appearance. It should be considered for background borders, salt barriers, groups or for untrimmed hedges to check foot traffic and assure privacy.

PROPAGATION - Increases are made by root cuttings, suckers, or by sowing cleaned seed in the fall.

BUTIA CAPITATA

Brazilian Butia*

DESCRIPTION - A striking palm, dwarf in size (to 12 feet) with long, graceful fronds which are light to bluish green in color. Short blunt spines occur along the base of the mid-rib of the fronds. The flowers are enclosed in a club-like drooping spathe, pointed at the lower end and about 2 to 3 feet long. In late spring, the spathe bursts open, revealing a much branched spike with yellowish flowers. In the fall, the yellow to orange fruits are about the size of a wild plum. The seeds are single, marble sized coconuts - each with three small eyes which evidently facilitate the entrance of moisture needed for germination. The trunks are crisscrossed with the butt ends of the old pruned off fronds. The base of the trunk is a bole which is not deeply buried. Fibrous roots branching from this bole are brown in color.

Brazilian Butia (*Butia capitata*) near the ocean
Myrtle Beach, South Carolina

NOTES - This species belongs to a group known as dry land palms. It is adapted to poor sandy soils. In rich moist soils, they are subject to disease.

This species survives transplanting better than the familiar cabbage palmetto (State Tree of South Carolina). Small specimens (2 to 3 feet) are best and easiest to transplant. Survival rates are usually very good. Nurserymen around Georgetown and Charleston, South Carolina, transplant this tree during the summer months. One stated a preference for July and August. The method used is to plant the bole in a shallow depression. This depression is useful to hold water which should be applied frequently during the first month or so.

As the season progresses, the depression is gradually filled in with sand. This will help to anchor the plant. The trunks of large specimens must be supported with anchoring wires. The older fronds are gradually trimmed off as new ones come out from the top. A hacksaw is an ideal tool for this job.

The palm is an introduced species. Each year plantings have been extended northward along the coast. The species seems to be at least as winter hardy as South Carolina's

Brazilian butia showing empty spathe and the large cluster of yellow fruit. Crescent Beach, South Carolina.

famous palmetto. Several years ago, several thousand were planted in the Wilmington - Carolina Beach area in North Carolina. The 8° and 9° temperatures in January of 1970 caused moderate injury which was observed at Carolina Beach and North Myrtle Beach. In some instances, all fronds were killed back. Later examination showed that almost all of these were recovering and putting out new leaves at the top. Several specimens in Morehead City, North Carolina, on the south side of a home showed only tip injury. However, these particular trees must be near the northern limit for the species.

Brazilian Butia can endure the direct salt winds in the Myrtle Beach - Charleston area. On North Carolina beaches (Wrightsville Beach and north), the plants will do best if given some protection from the north wind.

CONSERVATION USE - Brazilian Butia might add interest to a dune revegetation planting, but it does not have the desirable form for the job. It is most useful around beach buildings on well-managed grounds to add a gay tropical touch. They are planted as singles, in groups, or rows with plants about 12 feet apart. The light green leaves show up especially well against the dark evergreen background of live oak.

PROPAGATION - The fruits are collected in late September to mid October. After they have rotted down a bit, the fleshy part is removed and the clean nuts planted in nursery beds. There are indications that some of the seed take two years to germinate.

*(In nursery trade as *Cocos australis* - cocos or australis palm)

ILEX OPACA

American Holly

DESCRIPTION - This is our native holly which has long been a familiar part of the American Christmas scene. On optimum sites, it becomes a large tree with smooth gray bark and short spreading branches. In beach areas, its height is usually greatly reduced, often to a shrub-like form.

The leaves are oval in shape with large remote spiny teeth. They are dull green above, yellowish-green below, 2 to 4 inches long, stiff and leathery, and exhibit only moderate resistance to salt windburn. Small white flowers bloom in June and the dull red berries ripen in November. This species has the male and female flowers on separate plants.

American holly

American holly
(Ilex opaca).
Myrtle Beach
South Carolina

NOTES - Holly prefers part shade but will be satisfactory in full sun. The leaves will sometimes scald on a hot sunny day when the leaves are wet. American holly is slow growing, especially on coastal sands. Survival rate of bare-rooted transplants is low. The leaves cannot stand the direct blast of the ocean wind. For these reasons, American holly is not regarded as an important species for dune erosion control. It is almost always found in close association with other vegetation which shields it from the elements.

There are a number of selections in the trade which are perfectly acceptable at the beach. One of these much favored in the Georgetown, South Carolina, area is called 'Savannah.' Yellow fruited types offer pleasing contrast to the red fruited ones.

CONSERVATION USE - American holly may be used where it will be at least partially protected by buildings, walls, or other physical or vegetative barriers. In the beach profile, its natural habitat is in the tree or forest zone where it occurs as an understory tree. The fruit is a choice food of eastern nockingbird, cedar waxwing, and fair food of cardinal, flicker, robin, yellow-bellied sapsucker, hermit thrush, turkey, Bohemian waxwing, and red-bellied woodpecker (3).

In landscaping, it should be secured from the nursery as a 2 to 4 foot plant. This will also assure the owner that the plant will produce berries later on. Furthermore, wild holly plants are difficult to move. It is used primarily as single specimens or as an accent plant among lower growing shrubbery. The texture is medium.

PROPAGATION - American holly is propagated by taking cuttings from a female tree in July and August. Treatment with indole-3-butyric acid in talc greatly increases rooting success.

JUNIPERUS VIRGINIANA

Eastern Redcedar

DESCRIPTION - A native evergreen tree to 25 feet or more, but in exposed areas reduced to shrub form. It has both short, prickly, immature needles as well as the mature, softer, scale-like foliage. They are dark green to bluish green in color. Since the plant is dioecious (sexes occur on separate plants), the bule-green fruits which appear in fall occur only on female plants. The bark is gray and light brown, stringy and fibrous.

The heartwood is reddish-pink in color, fragrant and extremely rot resistant. The sap wood is white. Due to its slow growth in these poor sand soils, the outer band of sap wood is reduced, often less than 1/2 inch. The greatest portion of the trunk is heartwood.

NOTES - Eastern redcedar foliage is readily killed back by salty sea winds. Therefore, at the beach it is found behind dune or vegetative protection where it takes on a shrubby growth form. When growing with other native species, it will develop a shortened trunk with a "staghorn" or flat topped branch system.

Cedar grows remarkably well on the infertile dunes. This is partly due to its affinity for limey soils. The beach sands which usually have a high pH are much to its liking.

This fortunate adaptability elevates eastern redcedar to a rank of importance in dune revegetation work.

Eastern redcedar (*Juniperus virginiana)*
clipped by salt wind at Fort Macon, North Carolina

Eastern redcedar behind protection but showing top branch damage from salt wind. Fort Macon, North Carolina.

CONSERVATION USE - The usual practice is to introduce cedar only into beach dune areas which already are protected by grass or other vegetation. Transplanted seedlings rarely make it without such protection. Other woody species with more salt resistance may be included in the plantings to provide a taller barrier in the future. Planted in groups, cedar should have a spacing of 6 or 7 feet.

One publication (8) claims that the fruit is eaten by 68 birds. Verne Davison (3) lists the following: choice food of bluebird, purple finch, grosbeak (evening, pine), mockingbird, Townsend's solitaire, myrtle warbler, waxwing (Bohemian and cedar); fair food of cardinal, catbird, white-winged crossbill, crow (common, fish), flicker, flycatcher, ruffed grouse, yellow-bellied sapsucker, fox sparrow, starling, tree swallow, brown thrasher, and hermit thrush.

Redcedar at the beaches is found only occasionally in landscape plantings. Large specimens are usually remnants of the former native cover. Such mature trees have usually suffered injury due to the removal of other protecting vegetation. When used in landscaping, it should be planted on the lee side of cottages or behind other cover. It can be used as a specimen or background. Its foliage is fine in texture and almost identical with Pfitzers juniper.

PROPAGATION - Clean seed is planted in the fall. Seedling stock is generally available from the state forestry nurseries.

PERSEA BORBONIA

Redbay

DESCRIPTION - A large native evergreen tree to 60 feet in its optimum habitat. In beach areas it is often shrubby, combed to a smooth even height with companion vegetation or to 30 to 40 feet in rearward areas. Leaves are oblong, lance shaped, bright green and lustrous above, and pale and bluish below. They are leathery, 3 to 4 inches long, 3/4 to 1 1/2 inches wide with a narrow orange colored midrib and a stout red-brown stem. Leaves are often disfigured by an abnormal growth or gall.

Flowers are small and creamy white. The fruit is about 1/2 inch long, blue-black with flesh not readily separated from the ovoid, slightly point. With some age, the bark is dark red and deeply furrowed with irregular flat ridges between. The growth rate is moderately fast.

Redbay (*Persea borbonia*)
Emerald Isle, North Carolina

Redbay - leaves and fruit.

NOTES - Redbay has a very wide soil tolerance - from rich moist soils along streams and in swamps to coastal sand dune areas.

It is closely related to avocado. It has good promise for landscaping in beach areas. But the author has yet to find one which has been planted "on purpose." Its tolerance to salt spray is about that for live oak although the size of its leaves would subject it to more wind whipping. In dune areas close to the ocean, it seldom occurs alone but always as scattered shingles in the smooth trimmed canopy of other species such as yaupon, live oak, cedar, and myrtle.

CONSERVATION USE - Redbay has potential for dune erosion control work and is presently under test for this purpose. Transplants should be situated where they will have adequate wind and ocean spray protection. Its usefulness as an ornamental has largely been ignored. But its year around attractiveness could well be utilized on protected sites for tall borders or single specimens. Hunters are very familiar with its very high value for quail food. Bluebirds also use the fruits.

PROPAGATION - Redbay is produced by planting clean seed in the fall.

PINUS PINASTER

Cluster Pine

DESCRIPTION - Cluster pine is native along the western coast of France and the Mediterranean Basin. In its native habitat, the tree can grow to 100 feet, but along our beaches it is dwarfed usually to 25 feet or less. The branches are spreading and pendulous forming a pyramidal head. Branchlets are reddish brown. The needles are stiff and coarse, often twisted shining green, and 5 to 9 inches long. Cones are short stemmed, glossy brown, and vary from 4 to 7 inches in length.

NOTES - This pine, much used in England for seaside plantings, would seem to be ideal for beach work. A number of old plantings on the Outer Banks in North Carolina were only partially successful. An insect identified as a pine cone borer will attack the main stem of this species. Often the affected area is so

Cluster pine (*Pinus pinaster*). Nags Head, North Carolina.

riddled that the trunk will break off at this point. The insect is well known for its depredations on loblolly pine

Cluster pine (X 1/2)

cones. In Manteo, North Carolina, cluster pine planted in close association with loblolly was severely damaged. On the other hand, plantings on Bodie Island and away from native stands of loblolly are doing well. Their height is 15 to 20 feet. They are on pure dune sand, but about 300 yards from the ocean where the danger of salt spray is lessened.

Another extensive planting was established years ago near Fort Macon, North Carolina. These trees grew to 10 feet or more, but took considerable wind injury. As time went by, native vegetation gradually enveloped the planting. Nurserymen soon found that cluster pine was not as well adapted to inclement beach conditions as Japanese black pine (*Pinus thunbergi*). Since that time Japanese black pine is used almost exclusively by nurserymen for landscaping.

CONSERVATION USE - If given protection, this is a beautiful and interesting species and may best be used for accent or specimen plants. The long coarse needles and large cones are unique and very attractive. It is not well suited for revegation work unless the plantings are some distance from the ocean. In such cases, a spacing of 10 to 12 feet may be used.

PROPAGATION - Nurserymen spring plant clean seed which has been stratified (mixed with damp sand or peat) and refrigerated for 30 days before seeding.

PINUS THUNBERGI

Japanese Black Pine

DESCRIPTION - As the name indicates, this is an import from Japan. It is better adapted for beach work than our several native species. In its optimum habitat, it can reach 100 feet; but in beach plantings, it usually is topped off at less than 20 feet. The branches are wide spreading and pendulous, and the branchlets are orange-yellow in color. Needles are borne in clusters of two. They are 2 1/2 to 4 1/2 inches long, bright green, stiff and sharply pointed. The cones are 2 to 3 inches long. This species is relatively fast growing and at maturity has a picturesque form.

Japanese black pine (*Pinus thunbergi*).
Vigorous young trees at Emerald Isle, North Carolina.

Japanese black pine

NOTES - This is a very adaptable and hardy pine and will grow on a wide variety of soils under adverse conditions. It is more salt spray resistant than any of the native pines and is equal to or better in this respect than cluster pine. Evidently, nurserymen were late in discovering the value of this pine for landscaping. Judging from the size of plants at the beach, most of them were established within the past six years.

The form and texture of pine seems to have a universal appeal. Japanese black pine is no exception, and it is especially popular in the Atlantic Beach - Emerald Isle area in North Carolina.

Japanese black pine produces cones after four or five years of age. Fruiting and seed production is usually prolific.

Like many pines, this one is subject to tip moth damage. The moth's egg produces a small grub which burrows inside and kills the twig ends. Extensive injury produces a shrubby growth.

The larvae of the sawfly sometimes attack this species. These caterpillars are dull green with dark brown heads. They travel the stems in groups - eating off the needles as they go. Small infestations may be picked off by hand. If this is impractical, a good insecticide (such as sevin) should be used.

CONSERVATION USE - Japanese black pine is a favorite for beach beautification. It is often used in rows for borders on driveways, property lines, and screens with a rather close spacing of 4 to 6 feet. It is also interesting as a single specimen or in groups. Three year old dune plantings of this pine have survived. But growth has only been moderate.

PROPAGATION - It is propagated by planting stratified seed in nursery beds in the spring.

POPULUS ALBA

White Poplar

DESCRIPTION - A small freely branching tree to 35 feet, but usually 10 to 20 feet in beach areas. The bark of the trunk is light gray with roughened dark fissures near the base. Its leaves are deciduous, alternate, long stalked, ovate or three to five lobed, and sharp pointed.

They are coarsely and irregularly toothed, 2 1/4 to 4 inches long, dark green above and white-wooly beneath. When windblown, the leaves are silvery in appearance. The male and female flowers (catkins) appear on different trees. The fruit is a capsule containing cottony seeds which travel far and wide on the wind. The tree is a rapid grower, and it will spread aggressively from root sprouts to form colonies.

White poplar (*Populus alba)*.
Salter Path, North Carolina.

NOTES - On the beach - a weed is a weed indeed! Most anything which will stop and stabilize the drifting beach sands is useful. This applies to white poplar. While it is not highly regarded inland, at the beach it becomes a useful tree. White poplar has the ability to grow on a variety of poor sites. For example, flourishing colonies are often found on roadbanks. It is adapted from the mountains to the sea, and in beach communities it is found more frequently in North Carolina than in South Carolina.

White poplar has only fair resistance to salt windburn. It is especially susceptible in the establishment phase. Therefore, it must be planted where protected from direct salt spray.

White poplar

CONSERVATION USE - The aggressive spreading habit of this tree, coupled with its modest soil requirements, places this plant on the "beach list." But field tests indicate that it will require additional help to get established on the dunes. Favorable valley sites, added topsoil, and occasional watering and fertilization will have to be considered through the first two critical years.

Off the dunes on slightly better soils, these trees can be placed out of the direct wind for shade, in rows along roadways, as single specimens, etc.

PROPAGATION - White poplar is increased by cuttings of either hard or soft wood. In both cases, rooting may be increased by the use of the root inducing substance indole-3-acetic acid. In the spring, long whips stuck deeply in moist sand outdoors will produce a moderate percentage of living plants.

PRUNUS AUGUSTIFOLIA

Chickasaw Plum

DESCRIPTION - This is a small, twiggy tree of poor and especially sandy soil areas where its usual height is less than 8 feet. Sprouts from root suckers enable it to spread and produce dense thickets. The bark is smooth, reddish brown, and the twigs often tipped with sharp spurs. Leaves are lance shaped and trough-like, shinny green, less than 2 inches long, and finely toothed along the edges. Small white flowers precede the leaves in the spring. Fruit is a small plum, slender stemmed, red or yellow with soft juicy flesh which clings to the stone. They ripen in early summer.

Chickasaw plum (*Prunus augustifolia*).
Sullivans Island, South Carolina

NOTES - Chickasaw plum is not a winner as a formal landscape plant. Its encroachment into adjacent areas could also be troublesome. Yet, this spreading habit is a very desirable trait for dune revegetation. Small plants from root suckers usually will not survive well after transplanting from the wild. Deeper rooted seedlings would be much preferred.

Chickasaw plums

CONSERVATION USE - It should not be too difficult to establish colonies in dune valleys for permanent erosion protection and as a thorny barrier in places where foot traffic is undesirable. Chickasaw plum also provides thick, thorny protection and food for wildlife including quail, robin, brown thrasher, blue jay, and redheaded woodpecker (3).

PROPAGATION - This plum is increased by planting cleaned seed in the fall.

PRUNUS CAROLINIANA

Carolina Laurelcherry

DESCRIPTION - A handsome evergreen tree to about 30 feet but at the beach usually clipped at 10 to 15 feet or at the height of protective vegetation, buildings, or dunes. Leaves are elliptic, sharp pointed, leathery, dark shining green above, and paler beneath. Leaf margins are usually smooth or sometimes finely toothed, 2 to 4 1/2 inches long and 3/4 to 1 1/2 inches wide. Flowers which are small, creamy white and borne in numerous short racemes appear in early spring. The fruits are shiny black, oblong, and about 1/2 inch in diameter. Each contains a single stone. They mature in autumn and persist until the next bloom.

The tree is relatively round in shape, often nearly flat topped at the beach and produces a dense shade. The wilted leaves are poisonous if eaten.

Carolina laurelcherry (*Prunus caroliniana*).
Salter Path, North Carolina.

Carolina laurelcherry.

NOTES - Laurelcherry is a native and is quite common as a component in shrub and woodland zones along the coast. Its soil requirements are low. Even so, the vigor of its growth in dune plantings is disappointing. On these near sterile sites, topsoil, organic additives, and fertilizer must be used to improve the situation. The salt wind rating of laurelcherry in our table is three, indicating that it cannot stand the direct blast of the ocean wind. For these reasons, this plant is not a good choice for wholescale application in dune plantings. Low survival rates in early plantings was later solved by clipping off two-thirds of the leaves of bare rooted stock.

CONSERVATION USE - Laurelcherry may be used in the dune shrub zone with discrimination, and where the required site improvements are met. Around buildings and cottages it is extremely decorative for tall shady borders along roads, property lines (spacing 8 feet), or as groups or specimen plants. It may also be used for screens (spacing 3 to 4 feet) or tall clipped hedges (spacing 2 feet).

Laurelcherry fruit is a choice food of the bluebird, mockingbird, robin, cedar waxwing, and a fair food of ringbilled gull (3).

PROPAGATION - Clean seed is planted in late fall.

PRUNUS SEROTINA

Black Cherry

DESCRIPTION - A large native tree with smooth, dark brown, aromatic bark. The leaves are oblong, lance shaped, 2 1/2 to 4 1/2 inches long, firm, shining above, and with many small incurved teeth along the edges. Sometimes the midrib underneath is dense with fine brown fuzz. Small white flowers bloom in spikes at the end of short leafy branches of the current year. Purple-black cherries the size of a large pea ripen in July. Each has a single seed.

NOTES - Black cherry is fairly common near the coast in sand soils. Excellent examples have been observed on the Outer Banks and also at Myrtle Beach State Park in South Carolina, where the trees are within 100 yards of the ocean. There are three reasons for including it in

Black cherry (*Prunus serotina*) in bloom.

Black cherry with fruit

this list: It will thrive on poor sand soils, has moderate salt spray resistance, and the fruit has wildlife value. The leaves are poisonous to cattle if they are eaten in a wilted condition.

CONSERVATION USE - Black cherry is useful as a component in the shrub and tree zone if planted after some other protective vegetation has been established. The addition of a few groups of this species enhances the wildlife value of the cover. The cherries are a choice food of the bluebird, bobwhite, catbird, crow, flicker, grosbeak, ruffed grouse, blue jay, kingbird, mockingbird, oriole, robin, yellow-bellied sapsucker, white-throated sparrow, starling, summer tanager, brown thrasher, thrush (gray-cheeked, hermit, Swainson's, wood), veery, vireo (red-eyed, warbling), cedar waxwing, woodpecker (downy, hairy pileated, red-bellied, red-headed), and fair food of red-winged blackbird, great crested flycatcher, common grackle, sharp-tailed grouse, pheasant, prairie chicken, towhee, and turkey (3).

At some distance from the ocean, black cherry may be used as a shade tree. Frequent infestations by tent caterpillars is a disadvantage.

PROPAGATION - Increases are made by planting the cleaned seed in the fall.

QUERCUS VIRGINIANA

Live Oak

DESCRIPTION - A majestic, native, evergreen tree which, at the beach, is clipped and moulded to the height of protective dunes or other vegetation. Live oak is mostly shrubby in the proximity of the ocean to tall trees windblown and flat topped toward the rear. The branches are widespreading, often touching the ground. In the Nags Head area, one such "tree" had a trunk 7 inches thick, was 5 feet high, and about 20 feet wide with all but the leeward branches tapering to the ground around its perimeter. The plant has a heavy tap root which goes deep for food and moisture. The bark of the twigs is gray and that of the trunk is dark brown tinged with red and slightly furrowed. Leaves are leathery, dark shining green above, pale and pubsecent underneath. They are variable, 1 1/2 to 2 1/2 inches long, generally not toothed or lobed. Acorns are borne singly or in clusters. At maturity, they are dark brown, oblong to about 3/4 inch, with a cup that covers 1/3 to 1/2 of the acorn. The acorns are edible - and especially good if toasted (so say some of the older folks in Salter Path, North Carolina.)

NOTES - Live oak by many standards is the most beautiful tree in the South. It is abundant along the coast where it forms an important part of the natural flora. It will grow in poor sandy soil and prefers good drainage. The very slow growth is its chief shortcoming. The leaves are medium sensitive to salt spray accumulation. Where planted close to the ocean, it needs partial protection from direct wind.

Live oak (*Quercus virginiana*). Wind-trimmed to shrub size. Salter Path, North Carolina.

This is one of the few plants which can be seeded direct in sand dune valleys. The acorns should be collected as soon as ripe in the fall and planted as soon as possible. If plantings are to be delayed for several days, they should be put into a plastic bag and placed in a refrigerator. If delayed for more than a week, damp sand should be mixed with the acorns in the bags.

The acorns are planted about 1 1/2 inches deep in dune sand. They start to develop a tap root immediately. The tops of the plants will emerge the following spring to early summer. First year seedlings produce 2 to 4 inches of top growth with 8 to 12 inch tap roots. If plantings are made in thick beachgrass cover, mice may eat many of the nuts.

CONSERVATION USE - Either nursery-grown one year seedlings or acorns may be used as a start in establishing perennial woody dune vegetation. Planters might be used to distribute the acorns in rows with two, possibly three, nuts per linear foot. Or they may be planted two to a "hill." Seedlings should be placed in groups in desirable exposure locations. For beautification around buildings, they will require plenty of space and are probably best as single specimens or small groups. Balled and burlapped nursery stock should be used. They will do best on the lee side of buildings or other protective vegetation. Sea winds will sooner or later mould them and make them "grow away" from the ocean.

PROPAGATION - Seedlings are produced from fall planted acorns.

Live oak with acorns.

SABAL PALMETTO

Cabbage Palmetto

DESCRIPTION - South Carolina picked this species for its state tree. It is well adapted in North Carolina only south of Wilmington. This palmetto can grow to 30 feet or more but normally 10 to 20 feet at our beach areas. The trunk is straight, the upper protion protected by a network of persistent leaf petiole bases. The crown of the tree consists of leaves which are fan-shaped to a yard across. They are divided into segments and supported by stems several feet long.

The underground section of the trunk is a swollen base from which many small wiry roots arise.

Fruits are black, fleshy, 1/3 to 1/2 inch long and contain a single nut-like seed.

Cabbage palmetto (*Sabal palmetto*). Windy Hill, South Carolina.

NOTES - This palmetto lends a distinctive tropical touch to beach plantings. At the northern extension of its range, it often suffers cold injury. Its increasing vigor is apparent as one travels south from the North

Carolina state line. South Carolinians particularly favor this tree; very likely it is the most planted tree species in South Carolina's resort areas.

Resistance to salt wind damage is good, and it is well adapted to sandy dune soils. Even so, they respond well to added fertility.

Strangely enough, these plants are best transplanted in the summer. June and July are favorite months for this work. The heavy bole or butt of the trunk is set in a saucer-like depression which is gradually filled with sand as the plant grows. Tall plants must be guyed with wires until the new roots take hold. One Charleston nurseryman insists that 25 percent of all transplants will die. So, a landscape job using palmettos could be an interminable one!

Palmettos should be fertilized and then watered until they show signs of vigorous new growth.

CONSERVATION USE - They may be used as single specimens and are striking in rows or groups with a spacing of about 8 to 10 feet. They are often used as avenue trees or for shade around beach homes. At Myrtle Beach, some cottagers plant English ivy at the base of palmettos. These vines soon drape the trunks with pleasing evergreen cover. With protection from the wind, trumpet creeper may also be used in this way.

PROPAGATION - Sabal palmetto is increased by seed which is fall planted and may not germinate until the second year.

AMPELOPSIS ARBOREA

Peppervine

DESCRIPTION - Vine with finely cut double or triple compound leaves very similar to those of trumpet creeper. New leaf growth at the terminal ends of branches are bronze-red. This is a distinguishing characteristic. Tendrils enable it to overtop shrubs and climb into trees. Spring flowers are small, greenish-white and insignificant. Loose clusters of purple-black, shining berries ripen in October. The seed resemble those of grape. The vine spreads by root suckers.

Peppervine (*Ampelopsis arborea*) scrambling over shrubbery (eastern baccharis). Holdens Beach, North Carolina.

Peppervine

NOTES - This vine is found on most beach areas in the Carolinas. It prefers "flat" dune valleys and road shoulders where moisture is not too far from the surface. Once established in such a favored position, it will spread to drier adjoining areas. Without support, it will form a rather dense groundcover.

CONSERVATION USE - With a rating of three, peppervine has only fair salt wind resistance. For sand dune work, it should be confined to the valleys. A plant spacing of 4 to 6 feet will develop into a full cover in a few years. It may be planted with occasional groups of trees or shrubs for support. This will increase its wildlife and songbird value. Catbirds, mockingbirds, and wood thrushes have been observed eating the fruit - but there must be others for the berries disappear quickly when ripe.

Peppervine is formless in habit for landscape work. If properly trained and supported and placed behind a windbreak, its foliage is very decorative. If planted at the base of bare banks and roadcuts, it should spread upward to provide erosion protection.

PROPAGATION - Peppervine is propagated by sowing cleaned seed in the fall or by hardwood cuttings taken in August and September and put under glass.

CAMPSIS RADICANS

Common Trumpetcreeper, Cow-Itch

DESCRIPTION - A somewhat sparcely leaved vine at first but gradually increasing in leafiness. It will make good ground cover when unsupported, but is also high climbing by means of aerial roots. The plant develops a long taproot which enables it to go deep for moisture and food. Stems are light brown. Leaves are divided into 9 to 11 leaflets. Flowers are orange, trumpet shaped, and 3 to 4 inches long. Long, pointed pods dangle from the vines in fall. These contain the tightly packed double-winged seed.

NOTES - The vine is a familiar sight on utility poles, fence posts, etc. It will endure infertile, eroded, dry, acid, sandy sites. It is not plentiful in beach areas. This may be due to its partial susceptibility to salt spray injury.

Common trumpetcreeper (*Campsis radicans*) on an old dune near Kitty Hawk, North Carolina.

Trumpetcreeper with pods and flowers.

Some people are allergic to this species - especially if the leaves are handled when wet.

CONSERVATION USE - With some protection, its bright leaves and showy flowers trained up on posts and tree trunks make an interesting addition to any seaside garden. Humming birds are partial to the flowers.

Year-old seedlings were planted in dune test plots in the spring of 1971. These plants, with some runners to 8 feet, were the most vigorous of all species in the test. The amount of maintenance which they will require in the future is still to be determined. At present, trumpetcreeper has good potential for beach revegetation work.

PROPAGATION - Seeds planted in the fall sprout vigorously in spring. In addition, July or August cuttings from mature stems of the current year's growth root readily as do root cuttings taken in December.

CLEMATIS PANICULATA

Sweetautumn Clematis

DESCRIPTION - This high climbing vine is aptly named. The fragrant shower of small white flowers which bloom in August accounts for the popularity of this beautiful plant. Each flower has four main petals (actually sepals) which form a white cross about an inch in size. A cluster of the pollen bearing filaments is located in the center of the flower. Leaves and stems are light green. Each leaf is made up of five leaflets (sometimes three), which have smooth edges and more or less pointed tips. Twining leaf stems enable the plant to climb. The seeds which ripen in the fall have plume-like tails.

NOTES - This clematis is an introduction from Japan. Production of readily germinable seed is good. Volunteer seedlings are often found around a vine where the soil has been disturbed. Seedlings have also been found as volunteers in lawns. Like all viney clematis, the growth is "topheavy." Stems toward the bottom of the plant are usually quite bare. The stems may be trimmed back severely. This will not deter its bloom since it flowers on the current year's growth.

Clematis needs a well drained site. At the beach, topsoil must be mixed with the sand. This provides an ideal soil medium with a high pH. Some gardeners put a handful

Sweetautumn clematis (*Clematis paniculata*) (9/1/72)
climbing over a wall which faces the ocean
Emerald Isle, North Carolina.

of crushed seashells around the main stem of each plant. Full sunlight is required for a full canopy of blooms.

CONSERVATION USE - This vine is a landscape beautification subject. It must always be planted where it can cling to

Sweetautumn clematis

some support. In picking a planting site, it is well to remember that it is only moderately resistant to salt spray. It is used on trellises with other shrubs in front to hide the lower bare stems. Most often it is seen on fences or simply growing on other shrubbery. It is beautiful in a yard arrangement with bleached driftwood. If planted on the lee side of a salt resistant shrub, it will grow through it and form a canopy to a point where the exposure restricts its further spread.

PROPAGATION - Seed may be fall planted and mulched over winter with pine straw. In the early spring, the covering is removed. For a small number of plants, spring cuttings stuck in sand root easily. Late spring and summer cuttings do well also. Layering is also successful - in fact one gardener tells me that short branches cut off and stuck in the garden in the spring root quite well. Rooting of cuttings was improved by the use of indole-3-butyric acid (Hormodin No. 3).

EUONYMUS FORTUNEI

Wintercreeper

DESCRIPTION - A prostrate, evergreen vine with green stems which root at stem nodes. The leaves have serrated margins and are 1 to 2 inches long. They are leathery, dark green with whitish veins on the top side and a light colored undersurface. The plant will climb trees or walls by means of aerial roots. The growth rate is slow. Two excellent varieties are *E. fortunei 'radicans,'* common wintercreeper and *E. fortunei 'coloratus,'* purpleleaf wintercreeper, which has a reddish-purple leaf color in the winter.

A third variety, *E. fortunei 'vegetus,'* bigleaf wintercreeper, deserves special mention. It has rounded, bright green leaves 1 to 1 1/2 inches in diameter. They are thick and leathery. Without support it will grow as a semi-shrub to about 4 feet. But it is at its best on walls, fences, tree trunks, etc., where aerial holdfasts enable it to climb. In the fall the plant bears orange fruits. For this reason it is sometimes called evergreen bittersweet. It is a more vigorous grower than the other varieties.

Wintercreeper (*Euonymus fortunei 'radicans'*)

NOTES - Wintercreeper has a high salt wind tolerance and will grow in the sun or deep shade. It prefers a soil of moderate fertility plus organic matter and an adequate supply of moisture. Although it can get along with less,

Bigleaf wintercreeper

the addition of six or more inches of topsoil mixed with the sand will guarantee its success. Once established, the dense growth keeps out weed encroachment. It is almost maintenance free except for occasional clipping to control its spread. It does not seem to be as susceptible to euonymus scale as the shrub, evergreen euonymus.

CONSERVATION USE - This is one of the better groundcovers. It is especially useful for densely shaded areas. The low growth habit is often utilized in foundation or other group plantings to fill in the areas between taller shrubbery. It makes an excellent bank cover. A 16-inch spacing between plants is satisfactory.

PROPAGATION - The plant is easily propagated by layering or by pulling up and planting the rooted runners. Better root systems can be developed by setting out cuttings in individual containers and transplanting these after they begin vigorous growth. Cuttings are taken in the spring or later in July. They will root in four weeks.

GELSEMIUM SEMPERVIRENS

Carolina Jessamine, Yellow Jessamine

DESCRIPTION - The bright yellow flowers of this native woody vine led to its selection as the state flower of South Carolina. Branches are wirey, twining, and climbing sometimes to 20 feet or more. Narrow pointed leaves which are waxy, dark, and nearly evergreen turn to a dark wine color in winter. Fragrant trumpet shaped flowers bloom in early spring. The fruit is a flattened capsule less than 1 inch long and usually with a short beak. Without support, the vines will trail on the ground, "tacking down" at the nodes as they go.

The flowers, leaves, and roots are poisonous. The plant is rated as dangerous to all livestock. Growth rate is moderate to slow.

Carolina jessamine (*Gelsemium sempervirens*) Photo courtesy of Dr. J. W. Hardin, Botany Dept. North Carolina State University.

Carolina jessamine

NOTES - Carolina jessamine does well on dry sandy sites and will thrive in full sun or shade. It will not tolerate a frontal exposure to the sea wind.

CONSERVATION USE - It is planted chiefly for the beautiful profusion of its bloom. Since the vines flower more abundantly when supported, it is most often trained on trellises, posts, fences, or trees. Occasionally it is used for ground cover on banks. For such mass plantings, a 2 by 2 foot spacing is recommended.

PROPAGATION - Cuttings of mature wood are taken in late summer.

LONICERA SEMPERVIRENS

Trumpet Honeysuckle, Coral Honeysuckle, Woodbine

DESCRIPTION - A high climbing evergreen vine which is native to the Carolina Coastal Plain and Piedmont. Slender, trumpet-like, brilliant red-orange flowers, 1 1/2 to 2 inches long occur in terminal clusters and are in striking contrast to the foliage. Leaves and stems are smooth without hair; the leaves 2 to 3 inches long, oval to oblong, bluish underneath, opposite each other, and with the upper pairs grown together around the stem to form an unbroken collar.

Trumpet honeysuckle (*Lonicera sempervirens*)
in bloom within 200 feet of the ocean.
Yaupon Beach, North Carolina.

Trumpet honeysuckle

NOTES - Coral honeysuckle widely scattered, but seldom abundant, is a familiar site along fence rows and especially woodland edges where it does well in partial shade. The brilliant yet delicate flowers have long struck the fancy of gardeners. Many a trumpet honeysuckle has been abducted from its woodland home to later grace front yard mailbox and lamp post. The plant evidently does not have a high degree of salt spray resistance. Yet, at Surfside Beach, South Carolina, it was climbing all over yaupon holly within 100 yards of the ocean. Near Salter Path, North Carolina, it is found occasionally in the shrub and tree zone. At Yaupon Beach, North Carolina, a tangle of grape, Virginia creeper, and coral honeysuckle may be found within 200 feet of the high tide mark.

CONSERVATION USE - For landscaping, it is most often seen as a decoration for posts, fences, and trellises. Topsoil should be added to the sand to improve fertility and especially to provide better moisture conditions.

PROPAGATION - Cuttings of the current year's growth are taken in August. They root easily (5) especially if treated with indole-3-butyric acid.

PARTHENOCISSUS QUINQUEFOLIA

Virginia Creeper

DESCRIPTION - A very hardy, widely adapted vine, famous for the blazing beauty of its orange-red leaves in autumn. Leaves are borne on a long stem and consist of five leaflets which are up to 6 inches long. The edges are usually serrated above the middle half of the blade. The stems are high climbing and depend on some support to which they cling by tendrils and adhesive "hold fasts." Without something to climb on, Virginia creeper will produce a flat relatively dense ground cover which "tacks down" as it goes. A long, searching tap root enables the plant to endure on droughty sites. Small, greenish flowers in the spring produce open clusters of blue-black berries in the fall. Lustrous brown seeds resemble those of the grape.

NOTES - This is an outstanding vine for either erosion control or landscaping at the beach. It tolerates dry sandy sites. Resistance to salt spray is remarkable for this "thin-leaved" plant since salt resistance seems to be associated with plants which have leathery (coreacious) leaves. Only slight protection from the direct sea winds

Virginia creeper (*Parthenocissus quinquifolia*)
at the top of the frontal dune
Fort Macon, North Carolina.

Virginia creeper

is required. In 1971 dune planting tests, its survival (95 percent) and growth rate was well above average.

Virginia creeper is often found in the grass zone of dune areas where it grows flat on the sand in the small openings untended by grass. In rearward areas, one is more likely to find it in the trees or scrambling over shrubs. Vines crawling flat on the ground will produce a crop of fruit. Usually, the berries are more numerous if the vines are climbing.

CONSERVATION USE - Here is a top-flight choice for the revegetation of sand dunes. As a ground cover in areas without upright woody plants, the suggested spacing is 4 to 6 feet. Other adapted shrubs or trees may be interplanted in groups as support for the vines if desired.

The fruit is a very important bird food. Verne Davison (3) lists it as choice for bluebird, catbird, crow, flicker, great crested flycatcher, eastern kingbird, mockingbird, robin, yellow-bellied sapsucker, starling, brown thrasher, Swainson's thrush, red-eyed vireo, warbler (bay-brested, myrtle), woodpecker (downy, hairy, pileated, red-bellied), and fair food for chickadee, western kingbird, fox sparrow, tree swallow, thrush (hermit, wood), and turkey.

In beautification work, Virginia creeper is included where brilliant fall color is needed, or where a wall, post, or fence needs to be hidden. It will grow well on a trellis.

PROPAGATION - Plants are produced by fall planting the cleaned seed or by stratifying the seed in damp sand at about 40° for two months before planting in the spring. Softwood cuttings taken in late summer root easily under glass as do hardwood cuttings planted out of doors in early spring.

SMILAX AURICULATA

Wild Bamboo

DESCRIPTION - A tough, wiry, evergreen vine with tendrils but not high climbing. It occurs as a partial to almost full canopy on shrubs or by itself on the dune sand as a low flattened mound. The main stems are coarse, slightly angular in cross section and usually spineless. Leaves are oblong to oblong-lanceolate, often lobed near the base, and with tips abruptly rounded to a sharp point.

The tight clusters of dark blue to black berries have a light chalky coating and are about 1/4 inch in diameter. There are two, sometimes three, tan colored seeds inside, each enclosed in an elastic membranous sac. The fruit ripens after Christmas.

The stems arise from gnarled, woody tubers. Since there are no rhizomes, the plant will not spread to become a pest. The growth rate is slow.

The author observing wild bamboo (*Smilax auriculata*)
Emerald Isle, North Carolina.

NOTES - This native is completely at home on dune areas where it is very well adapted to sand and salt wind. The dark evergreen foliage makes a conspicuous addition to the seascape in the winter. Often, it will completely cover a small shrub to make a compact mound.

CONSERVATION USE - The excellent adaptation of this plant should make it a prime subject for beach work. When stock becomes available, it will be useful in dune cover plantings. Though almost thornless, it is rough and wiry enough for barriers to block or direct foot traffic away from critical areas where such use would destroy the dune cover. In landscaping, it may be used as a protective wind screen if trained up on a sturdy trellis or fence. There is also a place for it as a low evergreen cover on banks or in groups for dark green mass plantings.

The fruit of this smilax is ripe and available as a wildlife food during the leanest winter months. Heavy crops of the berries disappear entirely by mid April. The bird droppings are cleaned by rain and the undigested seeds of these berries are concentrated by the wind in dune hollows and along pavement edges. Mr. Lauris Joyner,

Wild bamboo with fruit

Park Ranger at Fort Macon State Park, has observed that during cold weather and when minnows are hard to come by, the sea gulls will come in flocks to feed on these fruits. All of this - the disappearance of heavy berry crops, the noticeable amount of "bird scarified" seed - and the gulls - have raised our appraisal of this plant as a wildlife food.

PROPAGATION - Early nursery seedings of this species, as well as subsequent nursery tests to induce germination, have failed. In May 1972, a row of newly emerged seedlings suddenly appeared in our beach plots. These were traced back to a seeding made in December 1969. It is now evident that the seed embryo of this species requires a long after-ripening period before it will sprout. In this case, the seeds were in the sand 2 1/2 years before they emerged. The planting depth of this test was about 2 inches. Only a few plants respond readily to direct seeding in the dunes. This seems to be one of them - though patience is a requirement.

VITIS AESTIVALIS

Summer Grape, Pigeon Grape

DESCRIPTION - A very vigorous, high-climbing vine with thick, rough, leathery leaves. They are up to 6 inches broad and shallowly or deeply three to five lobed. The undersides of the leaves are wooly and bluish to rusty colored. The tendrils are branched and the pith is not continuous through the nodes. The flower clusters up to 6 inches long are followed in September by small black grapes 1/4 to 1/2 inch in diameter.

Summer grape (*Vitis aestivalis*) climbing on bayberry shrubs Kitty Hawk, North Carolina.

NOTES - This vine is found throughout all provinces in the Carolinas. The most abundant occurrence on the beach was found around and north of Kill Devil Hill, North Carolina. Here it was thriving amidst the dunes and usually scrambling on or sometimes enveloping shrubby

Summer grape

vegetation. In other places, without support, it was growing flat on the sand, interwoven with grass and providing good ground cover. People in nearby Manteo once made special trips in the fall to pick these grapes for wine and jelly making.

This plant does well on beach sand and seems to withstand a high degree of salt wind exposure - at least equal to muscadine grape.

CONSERVATION USE - Since this vine is well adapted to beach conditions, it will be a valuable perennial for sand erosion control. For landscaping, it is ideal for trellis work or to train on fences, etc.

All wild grapes are good wildlife plants. Not only do many birds and several animals eat the berries, but its tangled growth on shrubs and trees make perfect nesting sites. Davison (3) lists it as a choice food for the cardinal, catbird, ruffed grouse, robin, brown thrasher, turkey, and red-bellied woodpecker.

PROPAGATION - Freshly collected and cleaned seed are fall planted, or hardwood cuttings are set under glass in November or March. The use of indole-3-butyric acid improved rooting of some grape species. Cuttings from the middle and basal parts of the shoots seem to root best (5).

VITIS ROTUNDIFOLIA

Muscadine Grape

DESCRIPTION - This grape is a perennial, deciduous, high climbing vine with tendrils and pith continuous through the nodes of the stems. Leaves are generally round in shape with conspicuous serrated edges and are light green in summer, turning to yellow in fall. Clusters of small greenish flowers bloom in May. The edible fruits which ripen in October are about 3/4 inches in diameter, dark purple, round with one to four seeds. Strangely, some plants are male, some female, while still others have perfect flowers with the necessary equipment of both sexes.

Muscadine grape (*Vitis rotundifolia*)
Hammocks Beach State Park, North Carolina.

NOTES - Early explorers of the Carolina seacoast were impressed with the prolific abundance of grapes. The species is still abundant and well adapted in our coastal sand dune country. Local people harvest these for wine and jelly making. Muscadines do well on sandy soil and can endure moderate exposure to salt laden winds. Most vines are found in the shrub and tree zones where they find support and protection. Without support, muscadine grape will grow flat on the dunes and act as a low ground cover.

Muscadine vine with immature fruit

CONSERVATION USE - For sand dune cover, muscadine grape is planted with or without other shrubs or trees for support. If used alone, a 4 or 5 foot spacing will be sufficient. Climbing vines produce more grapes and the tangled mass of stems will be favored by birds for nesting. The fruit is a choice food of the cardinal, grackle, bluejay, summer tanager, towhee, turkey, and red-bellied woodpecker (3). A number of small mammals also eat this grape.

Other interesting uses of this plant is for screening or beautification where the stems are supported by a fence or trellis. An outdoor area may also be shaded by training the vines on a roof-like arbor.

PROPAGATION - The clean seed are sown in the fall. Hardwood cuttings in early spring are also used. Those from middle and lower stem sections are best. Treatment with indole-3-butyric acid helps rooting. Layering, by partially twisting a branch to crack it lengthwise and burying the injured section, is usually successful.

ARTEMISIA STELLERIANA

Dustymiller, Beach Wormwood

DESCRIPTION - A herbaceous perennial to 2 1/2 feet. Leaves and stems are covered with a white wooly coating giving the plant a silvery-white appearance. Small yellow or white flowers are borne on single spikes which may be compressed or loose and many-branched. Leaves are aromatic and finely divided or deeply lobed depending on the variety. The plant spreads by means of rhizomes.

There are several varieties of dustymiller. Of greatest interest to the seaside gardener is the common form with flowering stalks to about 1 foot. The shorter white-leaved sprouts from underground rhizomes enable the plant to spread widely to form a loosely knit ground cover. A common upright variety is 'Silverdust.' In addition, there are a number of interesting species to select from.

NOTES - The best beach Artemisias are those with the grayish-white leaves. The color is due to the copious leaf covering of fine silvery down. These catch the droplets of salt spray. After evaporation, the tiny salt crystal falls harmlessly to the ground. Creeping dustymiller was seen mixed with American beachgrass on the seaward side of the first dune at Nags Head, North Carolina (see photo).

The bright leaf color provides interesting contrast for rock gardens, borders, and edging for walks and flower beds. It will thrive in the most ordinary conditions including very dry, infertile sites. It prefers a sunny location.

PROPAGATION - Propagation is by division, cuttings, or seed.

Artemisias TOP: Spreading in beachgrass at Nags Head, North Carolina.
BOTTOM: In gardens at Myrtle Beach, South Carolina. The species at the top and lower right spread by rhizomes.

CORTADERIA SELLOANA

Selloa Pampasgrass

DESCRIPTION - The photograph of this species serves much better than a written description. The grass grows in large clumps with the numerous leaves arising mostly from the base. The seed stems can grow up to 8 feet tall. Short heavy tillers sprouting from the crown cause the clumps to enlarge slowly. Large, feathery, silvery-white seed plumes appear in September. These are very decorative. The seed do not seem to be viable.

Selloa Pampasgrass (*Cortaderia selloana*)

NOTES - This is a very popular landscape plant along the Carolina coast and especially prominent in the Myrtle Beach area. The grass was originally brought to this country from Argentina. The leaves stay half green in the winter. During the summer, the leaf tips usually show salt windburn where the grass is in an exposed position.

At any rate, some wind protection is needed to keep the seed plume from becoming tattered.

CONSERVATION USE - Since we have native grasses which are better adapted for sand stilling, pampasgrass is not used for this purpose. It is used quite extensively around beach homes, motels, and such. Where accent is needed, its silvery plume is as effective as waving a flag. One often sees it in groups which include yuccas and smaller evergreen shrubs.

PROPAGATION - This grass is propagated by division - each stubby tiller with a few roots attached will make a plant.

ERYNGIUM MARITIMUM

Seaholly Eryngo, Seaholly

DESCRIPTION - Seaholly is a herbaceous perennial of the parsley family which spreads by underground rhizomes. The plant grows to about 3 feet in height and is much branched. The stiff, chalky-blue leaves are somewhat fleshy. They have white margins and veins and are coarsely spiney along the edges. Small purple-white flowers are found in tight clusters at the branch ends. Beneath each is a star shaped collar of leaf like, spine tipped bracts.

NOTES - This unique plant is included as a "conversation piece" since its natural occurrence at Nags Head, North Carolina, has caused some interest and inquiry. Radford et al., (6) report it as a "very rare intorduction, sparse on the beach dunes; Dare County, North Carolina." It was brought in from Europe by accident and is said to be more common in the New York area. It is evidently better adapted in that more northern section than in the Carolinas. As the situation now stands, it cannot be recommended for use south of Dare County, North Carolina. Plants at Emerald Isle, North Carolina, are growing but seem to lack the vigor of those at Nags Head.

CONSERVATION USE - The striking appearance of this plant gives it a high value in the eyes of seaside garden enthusiasts. It would be appropriate in combinations with yuccas, and both gray and green cypress lavendercottons. Dark green backgrounds would emphasize the color and design of its leaves. It can be useful for dry dune bank

Seaholly (*Eryngium maritimum*) on the dunes
Nags Head, North Carolina

Seaholly

cover; however, it must be remembered that it dies to the ground each winter. It will grow on the dunes without the addition of topsoil.

PROPAGATION - Seaholly evidently produces viable seeds since that is the means by which it has spread. To get only a few plants, it is easier to dig and transplant the sprouts from rhizomes.

HEMEROCALLIS FULVA

Tawny Daylily

DESCRIPTION - A herbaceous perennial lily which spreads by rhizomes to form relatively dense colonies about 18 inches tall. Leaves are bright green, arching, narrow, and elongated; 1 to 2 feet or more long and up to an inch wide. The orange, trumpet shaped flowers are borne on tall stalks. Fruit does not develop regularly in this species. The roots are thick and fleshy with tuberous swellings.

NOTES - Daylilies do well in almost any situation, half shade or sun, good soil or poor. They require little care. Where growth is robust, the plants should be lifted and divided every three or four years. The old fashioned, single orange lily has escaped from cultivation and is found along roadsides and old home places. It is one of the more vigorous spreading types. At the beach, daylilies require some soil improvement and shielding from salt spray.

CONSERVATION USE - Daylily is quite common in seashore gardens in the Carolinas. Its adaptability to these conditions is quite well known. It is used for mass, bank, or border planting but is not adapted for dune work since it requires sea wind protection and soil amendments.

PROPAGATION - Increases are made by division of the roots.

Daylily (*Hemerocallis fulva*) in foreground.
Japanese black pine around cottage.
Emerald Isle, North Carolina.

HYDROCOTYLE BONARIENSIS

Largeleaf Pennywort

DESCRIPTION - A very "busy" little herbaceous ground creeper which spreads by means of far reaching underground stems. Height of the growth is about 6 inches. Leaves are bright shiny green, slightly scalloped along the edge, almost round (1 1/4 to 4 inches across), and supported in the middle underside by a long single petiole arising directly from the ground. Underground stems are white. The flowers are small, pale white-green on a single stem from the soil surface, branching near the top and usually as tall or taller than the leaves.

All above ground parts of the plant die back in the winter.

NOTES - This species is found almost exclusively along the coast and is rare inland. It prefers moist sandy areas among beach dunes and along beach roads. However, it will grow well on the higher and dryer dunes along with

Largeleaf pennywort (*Hydrocotyle bonariensis*)
Sunset Beach, North Carolina.

Largeleaf pennywort showing underground
rhizome and flowering habit.

the other native vegetation. No salt spray damage to the leaves has been observed - an indication of its high tolerance in this respect.

Pennywort responds vigorously to additions of topsoil, fertilizer, and water. If planted in a landscaping bed or garden, it may well run everything else out. Yet, if controlled, it can be used effectively as a mass planting where foot traffic is curtailed.

CONSERVATION USE - For sand stilling work, it is insufficient by itself but useful as a companion with other plants. Only a few roots planted at 10 foot intervals or so will quickly infiltrate and strengthen a thin stand of native vegetation. Once established on the dunes, pennywort requires no maintenance.

PROPAGATION - The plant is spread by digging and transplanting the rhizomes.

HYMENOCALLIS CALATHINA

Basketflower

DESCRIPTION - Basketflower is a perennial lily which was brought to this country from Peru and Bolivia. The bulb is long-necked, with six to eight leaves 1 1/2 to 2 1/2 feet long, fleshy, light green, and 2 inches or more wide. Flower stalks are about 2 feet long surmounted by a cluster of two to five white flowers all arising from a single cup. The long tube of each flower is separated at the summit into narrow, strap-like, recurved petals.

The plants are killed to the ground each winter. Growth rate is fast. The formation of off-shoots on the bulbs gives rise to a dense mass of leaves.

NOTES - Only a single planting of this species was observed at Folly Beach, South Carolina. Its appearance was so striking that it was included in this list. On this site it was growing vigorously within 150 feet of the ocean.

It requires a well drained site. A little topsoil mixed with beach sand will meet these requirements. Since it dies to the ground in the winter, we see no reason why it would not be adapted to the entire coastline of the Carolinas.

CONSERVATION USE - Menninger (13) has a high regard for its salt spray resistance and values it as a good species

Basketflower (*Hymenocallis calathina*)
Folly Beach, South Carolina.

Basketflower

for the low front row of a vegetative salt wind barrier. The plant may be used in groups but is especially good in rows for borders.

PROPAGATION - Plants are increased by digging and separating the offshoots from the bulbs. They transplant easily - even the smallest pieces root readily.

IBERIS SEMPERVIRENS

Evergreen Candytuft

DESCRIPTION - A low growing ground cover to 1 foot and characterized by its dense mass of small, white flowers which occur in elongating racemes or spikes during the early spring. The foliage is narrow and about an inch long. It does not spread from the root system but instead by branches which bend down and take root.

Evergreen candytuft (*Iberis sempervirens*)

NOTES - Once evergreen candytuft has become established, it should be left alone. A moderately rich and moist soil seems to be its major requirements. It grows best in the sun. After flowering, a light clipping will help to produce a dense growth.

Evergreen candytuft

CONSERVATION USE - It is used almost exclusively for borders. In seaside gardens, it is not bothered too much by the salt spray; but it will need a generous amount of topsoil mixed with the sand.

PROPAGATION - Increases are made by division, cuttings, or seed planted in the spring.

LIPPIA NODIFLORA

Lippia

DESCRIPTION - Lippia is a perennial native ground creeper with long runners which root at the nodes. The leaves also occur at the nodes and are 1/2 to 1 1/2 inches long, dark green, elongated, wedge shaped with definite teeth along the margin of the upper half. An erect flower stem from the node bears a single 1/4 to 1 inch cylinder of tiny dark purple flowers with white anthers. The leaves and most aerial stems which are not in contact with the soil die back in the winter.

NOTES - The plant is a fast grower. One year runners often grow to 8 feet or more. The flat creeping habit enables the plant to withstand mowing and a moderate amount of foot traffic. It can be a pest in a good lawn, but is often a welcome addition to unthrifty ones. The plant will survive on pure dune soil but is stringy under these conditions. Optimum sites are valleys between dunes or flats where better moisture conditions are available. Lippia responds well to added fertility and does best in full sun to partial shade.

Lippia (*Lippia nodiflora*)
Emerald Isle, North Carolina.

Lippia

CONSERVATION USE - Lippia may be used for groundcover where the sand has had little improvement. It will become weedy on better soil areas where other garden plants are grown. The spread of this plant is controlled by pulling up the long surface runners.

PROPAGATION - Rooted portions of the runners are pulled up and transplanted during the spring and early summer.

SANTOLINA CHAMAECYPARISSUS

Cypress Lavendercotton

DESCRIPTION - A much branched compact, silver-gray plant to 2 feet which was brought to this country from the Mediterranean region. The linear leaves are evergreen, fine wooly, 1/2 to 1 1/2 inches long and crowded with tiny leaflets. Flowers which come in June, extend beyond the body of the foliage, are button like and drab-yellow in color. Drooping stems will root where they touch the soil. This enables the plant to spread slowly. The foliage is highly aromatic. Growth rate is moderate.

Another interesting species is *Santolina virens* which has the same general habit of growth but is bright green instead of gray. It is probably not as salt tolerant as lavendercotton since it lacks the protective wooliness.

Cypress lavendercotton (*Santolina chamaecyparissus*) mixed with yuccas along a Myrtle Beach highway.

Cypress lavendercotton

NOTES - Lavendercotton with its fine coat of gray hair seems impervious to salty sea breezes. It likes a dry rather infertile site, a preference in which it can readily be accommodated at the beach. In fact, overwatering or excessive fertilizing will cause it to fall apart or even die.

CONSERVATION USE - The color and stature of this species reminds one of the desert. It fits perfectly with yuccas. In fact, one often sees such groups on highway medians.

It is an excellent rock garden or bank plant or used in foreground plantings for foliage effect, for borders, or simply as specimens where its color will provide contrast.

PROPAGATION - This plant is increased by cuttings taken in the spring or just before frost in the fall.

REFERENCE LIST

(1) Wyman, Donald. *Shrubs and Vines for American Gardens*. New York: Macmillan Co., 1969.

(2) Wyman, Donald. *Ground Cover Plants*. New York: Macmillan Co., 1956.

(3) Davison, Verne E. *Attracting Birds: From the Prairies to the Atlantic*. New York: Thomas Y. Crowell Co., 1967.

(4) Bailey, L. H. *The Standard Cyclopedia of Horticulture*. New York: Macmillan Co., 1933.

(5) Doran, W. L. *Propagation of Woody Plants by Cuttings*. Expt. Stu. Bull. No. 491; Amherst, Massachusetts: U. of Mass., College of Agric., 1937

(6) Radford, A. E.; Ahles, H. E.; Bell, C. R. *Manual of the Vascular Flora of the Carolinas*. Chapel Hill, North Carolina: Univ. of N. C. Press, 1968.

(7) Hardin, J. W. *Stock-Poisoning Plants of North Carolina*. Bull 414 Rev. Ag. Expt. Sta. Raleigh, N. C.: N. C. State Univ., 1966.

(8) *Invite Birds to Your Home*. USDA-SCS, Pamphlet 940. Washington, D. C.: Supt. of Documents, 1969.

(9) Boyce, S. C. *The Salt Spray Community*. Ecol. Mong. 24:29-67, 1954.

(10) Davis, Dr. John H. *Dune Formation and Stabilization by Vegetation and Planting*. U. of Florida, Gainsville, Fla: Tech. Memo No. 101, Dept. of the Army, Corps of Engineers, 1960.

(11) Jones, E. V., et al. *Lawn Grasses for South Carolina*. Circular 495, Clemson University, USDA Extension Service, Clemson, S. C., 1970.

(12) Blake, C. T., et al. Circular 292, Raleigh, N. C.: N. C. State Univ., USDA Extension Service, 1971.

(13) Menninger, E. A. *Seaside Plants of the World*. New York: Hearthside Press, Inc., 1964.

(14) Stoesz, A. D.; Brown, R. L. *Stabilizing Sand Dunes*. In A. Stefferud (ed.) USDA Yearbook of Agri. pp. 321-326, 1957.

(15) Sharpe, W. Curtis. *Plant Materials Activities in the Mid-Atlantic States*. USDA-SCS, Annual Technical Report, 1969.

(16) Hartman, A. T.; Kester, D. E. *Plant Propagation Principles and Practices*. Englewood Cliffs, N. J.: Prentice-Hall, Inc., 1959.

INDEX